Construction Companion to Building Surveys

Mike Hoxley

RIBA Publications

© Mike Hoxley 2002

Published by RIBA Companies Ltd, which trades under the name of
'RIBA Publications', 1–3 Dufferin Street, London EC1Y 8NA

ISBN 1 85946 091 7

Product Code: 22367

British Library Cataloguing in Publication Data.
A catalogue record of this book is available from the British Library.

Publisher: Mark Lane
Editor: Lionel Browne
Series Editor: David Chappell
Commissioning Editor: Matthew Thompson
Project Editor: Katy Banyard
Designer: Bettina Hovgaard-Peterson

Typeset, printed and bound by Hobbs the Printers, Hampshire

Contents

Foreword

This is the third of a series of guides being produced by RIBA Publications under the general heading of *Construction Companion*. They are intended to be compact and accessible guides written in plain language, but each one authoritative in its own subject.

Despite the proliferation of legal cases dealing with failures to carry out this type of work properly, building surveys are still treated very casually by many architects. I do not recall the topic being treated with a great deal of seriousness during my time as a student either (a long time ago now, but things do not appear to have changed much). Although this is a small book, a lot of material is packed into it. Every aspect of the subject is covered, from the equipment needed to carry out the survey, through the methods to be employed, to the writing of the final report. A very useful chapter describes the many different surveys that may be required. Every survey requires proper preparation; a casual approach is definitely not required.

This is no academic treatise, but a practical guide to be used on a daily basis whenever building surveys are undertaken. The author draws on his considerable experience to give really useful pointers to – among other things – the differing causes of dampness, movement in buildings, timber defects and roof problems.

The book closes with an actual building survey report, which the author subjects to a rigorous analysis. The many different ways in which the writer of the report is exposed to potential legal action are quite frightening. For me, and I suspect for most architects, this is probably the most useful part of the book.

Dr Mike Hoxley is a leading authority in this field. What he does not know about building surveys is probably of little importance. He appears to have performed the amazing feat of cramming a great deal of what he knows into this book in wonderfully straightforward terms, so that it comes close to being the only book the average architect actually needs on this topic

David Chappell BA(Hons Arch) MA(Arch) MA(Law) PhD RIBA
Series Editor

Preface

Advances in technology have made huge differences to many traditional industries, and today's world of work would be largely unrecognisable to many workers of only a few generations ago. It is also true, however, that the pace of change in the construction industry has been slower than in most, and to some extent the same can be said of the industry's professions. Of course computer-aided design, word processing and mobile telephones have altered the work of such professionals, but the world of surveying seems set to have a huge revolution imposed upon it. The author is honoured to have been commissioned by RIBA Publications to write this handbook at such a pivotal time as far as the surveying professions are concerned.

By the 'surveying professions' the author refers to any built environment professionals able and inclined to *survey* property. Such professionals will include architects, chartered surveyors, engineers and chartered builders, and throughout this book the term *surveyor* is intended to refer to any such professional carrying out a survey. In Chapter 4 the core knowledge that the surveyor requires is discussed. The surveyor's most important subject area is construction technology – without this the surveyor cannot function. It is the author's very firmly held conviction that elementary construction technology (that is, domestic building technology) is by far the most important subject studied on any built environment professional degree course. In every case where the author has been called in to advise on the professional negligence of a surveyor, the main problem has been a failure to understand (or perhaps more importantly to remember) basic principles of construction technology. Certainly those slips-ups that the author has made himself have been due to this basic problem. This book is not intended to provide this knowledge, and it is assumed that the reader will have a sound knowledge of construction technology before considering undertaking a survey. What the book *will* attempt to do is to point out the areas of technology that, at their peril, are most often ignored by professionals when carrying out surveys.

MH

Acknowledgements

The author acknowledges the further sacrifices of his family (Susan, Chris, Rachel and Claire) that have enabled this book to be completed. The book is dedicated to David Bullen and Mary Baker, with whom the author served his 'apprenticeship' in surveying buildings.

The author gratefully acknowledges copyright permissions for the use of the following:

Building Research Establishment for Tables 1 and 2 of BRE Digest 251

CIRIA for Figures 12 and 13 from Publication R1 11, *Structural Renovation of Industrial Buildings* (this document may be obtained from CIRIA, 6 Storey's Gate, Westminster, London SW1P 3AU; tel 020 7222 8891)

Association of British Insurers for domestic subsidence data

Surveyors and Valuers Accreditation for benchmark standards for the Homebuyer Survey and Valuation

1   Purpose of survey

1.1   A time of change

Surveys can be broadly classified into two main types: those where condition is assessed, and those where measurements are recorded. Each of these two types will be considered briefly in this introductory chapter, but it is in condition surveys that the revolution referred to in the Preface is about to take place.

1.2   Assessment of condition

Traditionally it has been just before a property is transferred that assessment of its condition has occurred, and the proposed changes will not significantly alter the timing of the activity. However, who commissions the service is set to change completely in the future. Traditionally the buyer has paid for and arranged the survey of a dwelling, but from 2004 or 2005 under government proposals when any home in England or Wales is sold it will be the seller who commissions the survey.

The main requirement of the Homes Bill is that it will be a criminal offence for any seller or seller's agent to offer for sale any home that does not have an information pack compiled. The contents of this pack will include copies of title documents, replies to standard preliminary enquires, a local authority search, copies of any statutory consents, warranties and guarantees, a draft contract and a *home condition report* (HCR). The HCR will be prepared by any surveyor accredited by the Home Inspectors Certification Board, and in addition to being contained within the pack it will also be stored in a digital version on a central database. Potential buyers of the home will be issued with a PIN (personal identification number) specific to that home, and will be able to access and download their own copy of the report over the Internet. Surveyors wishing to undertake this work will therefore need access to the necessary technology to e-mail their report to the central database.

There are about 4,500 surveyors carrying out residential surveys in England and Wales at present, but only some 30% or so of buyers commission surveys. Most buyers who buy with a mortgage prefer to risk relying upon their lender's much less detailed valuation report. It is estimated that between 2,500 and 4,500 additional surveyors will be required in England and Wales to cope with the increased workload that these changes will bring.

The progress of the Homes Bill was delayed by the 2001 General Election, but a pledge to reintroduce it was contained in the re-elected Labour Government's manifesto. In August 2001 the Government announced its continued commitment to the proposed legislation, and said that seller's information packs would be required by late 2004 or early 2005.

As one would expect, there is to be a prescribed format for the HCR, although in detail it is similar to the intermediate type of survey discussed in section 2.2.2. These changes have occurred at a time when there is in any event much greater prescription in the format of survey reports driven by professional indemnity insurers (see Chapter 3), a move towards 'hidden defects insurance', and adverse media publicity about surveyors generally. It is likely that the days of an individually tailored style of condition report are nearing their end. As discussed in Chapter 2, even the Society for the Protection of Ancient Buildings (SPAB) is proposing to introduce a standard report format for condition surveys of historic buildings.

There are 20 million or so homes in England alone, and far more dwellings are surveyed than any other type of property. The proposed changes contained in the Homes Bill will completely alter the process of, and market for, residential surveys, but of course there are many other types of building that require assessment of their condition. At the time of sale it is likely that the buyer of the freehold or a leasehold interest of a non-residential building will continue to commission the survey. However, the long-standing legal principle of *caveat emptor* (buyer beware) will be stood completely on its head by the proposed homes legislation, and it will be interesting to see whether there are further developments in this direction with non-residential property in the future.

Besides transfer of ownership the other main times at which the assessment of condition is required are prior to the carrying out of building or engineering works on adjacent or nearby land, and during or at the end of a lease to assess legal responsibility for repair (dilapidations). Of course there may well be other occasions when the owner of a building wishes to commission an inspection for some other purpose (say for example because they are concerned about a particular defect).

1.3   Measured surveys

Although a full measured survey may be carried out as part of a condition survey, it is more likely to be carried out prior to the design of alteration or extension work. Both horizontal and vertical dimensions are recorded: Figure 1.1 shows an example of the dimensions to be recorded in a typical room. Note that running dimensions are taken wherever possible, as these are more accurate and there is less scope for errors to creep in. Both diagonals are measured in each room to ensure accurate plotting of the room, which may not be completely square. The floor to ceiling height is recorded in each room, and usually the head and sill

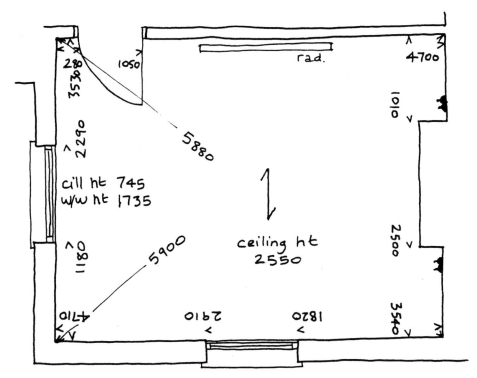

Figure 1.1 Sketch for measured survey of room

heights of all windows. The direction of span of floor joists should be noted, taking care to check for any over-boarding (an additional layer of boarding, fixed above and at right angles to the original boarding) in particularly old buildings. The thickness of all internal and external walls should be recorded; the extent of the recording of services will depend upon the exact purpose of the survey. It is sensible to record the positions of radiators and electrical fittings, as in Figure 1.1, since these have an unfortunate habit of being located precisely in the position where a door opening is planned.

It is usual to sketch on graph paper the floor layout of each storey of the building being surveyed before taking any measurements. Care is required to ensure that the sketch is to the correct proportions, as this will reduce any confusion when the plan is plotted back in the office. A measured survey is not to be rushed, and the more care is taken to ensure accuracy the easier the task of plotting will be.

Figure 1.2 indicates the dimensions to be recorded when measuring an elevation. Of course all the horizontal dimensions are checks of what has been recorded internally, but not all the vertical measurements can be taken internally. If a levelling survey is being carried out at the same time then the most accurate method of recording the vertical measurements is simply to invert the staff and place the

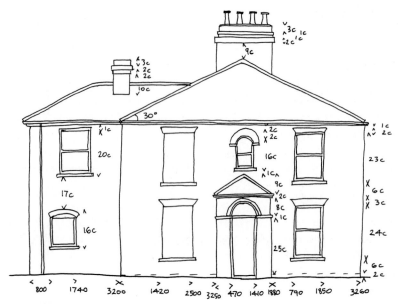

Figure 1.2 Sketch for measured survey of elevation

base of it on the feature whose height is being checked. This is sometimes the only method of recording the vertical measurements, particularly when the building is not faced with brickwork. The operation is then of course a two-person job. Where the elevations are of brickwork then the brick courses can be counted (as in Figure 1.2). The exact height of a course (usually about 75 mm) should then be checked and this dimension used when drawing up the elevations. With inaccessible features such as high-level parapet walls or chimney stacks, counting courses is very often the only practical method of surveying (unless ladders or mechanical platforms are to be used). The equipment needed to carry out measured surveys is discussed in Chapter 6.

1.4   Summary

In this introductory chapter the purpose of the survey has been considered and the significant shift in emphasis away from 'buyer commissioned' to 'seller commissioned' residential surveys has been discussed. This change – imposed by statute – will increase the workload of surveyors and hasten the trend towards prescribed and standardised report layouts. The process of carrying out measured surveys has been outlined; in the next chapter the various types of condition survey are discussed in greater detail.

2 Types of survey

2.1 Definitions

The various types of survey undertaken by the surveyor were considered at length by the Construction Industry Council (CIC) in 1997.[1] The CIC is a representative forum for the construction professions (including architects, engineers and surveyors), and after much discussion produced a document entitled *Definitions of Inspections and Surveys of Buildings*. Up until that time there was some confusion over the terms used to describe the relatively large number of types of inspection it is possible to undertake. For example, a layperson might reasonably have expected a 'structural survey' to be carried out by a structural engineer, but in fact many chartered surveyors were carrying out inspections that they described as 'structural surveys'. This confusion was not solely in the minds of clients, as different professions were calling the same type of inspection by different names. One of the intentions of the CIC document was to urge members of the professional bodies not to continue to use the term 'structural survey'. Of course there will be some practitioners who will be slow to change, and readers may be aware of cases where the old descriptions are still being used. However, there are signs that the industry has started to move to adopt the terms recommended by the CIC, and it is these titles that will used throughout this book and which are presented below.

2.2 Domestic surveys

Most property inspections carried out in the UK are of houses, and the three main types of survey undertaken on residential property will be considered first. These are:

- the valuation
- the property purchase survey and valuation
- the building survey.

As indicated in Chapter 1 there are proposals by government to legislate to alter significantly the house-selling process in England and Wales in the near future. These proposals will introduce another type of survey, which will be discussed after consideration of the three main types of survey currently carried out.

2.2.1 Valuation

At present about seven out of ten house purchasers rely solely on the valuation carried out by their mortgage company surveyor. However, the purpose of this inspection is not to assess condition but rather to estimate values – usually the current market value and the reinstatement value for insurance purposes (see section 2.6 below). Not all valuations are carried out by a surveyor acting for the mortgage company, but in all cases the inspection, research and report will follow a similar format. Where the property inspected is for rent rather than for sale the main purpose of the valuation will be to ascertain that the rental value is a true reflection of the property's market value.

The inspection is fairly brief, and it is the research required to discover the recent selling price of similar properties in the same locality that is more important. Some mortgage companies insist on this comparable evidence being submitted with the mortgage valuation report. The valuation inspection will take account of relevant factors affecting condition, location and aspects of construction that are readily observable on a walk-round inspection. The report (usually on a standard preprinted form) may be prepared by a surveyor employed directly by the mortgage company (a staff valuer) or by a panel valuer, who is a surveyor employed by a consultancy approved by the mortgage company. There was a Monopolies and Mergers Commission investigation in 1994 to ascertain whether building societies and banks were operating in an anti-competitive manner by allowing only staff and panel valuers to act for them; the Commission concluded that they were not. Had the Commission decided otherwise then it would have been possible for a prospective purchaser to arrange their own valuation report from an independent surveyor. It can be very difficult for consultants to be appointed to the panel of a particular mortgage lender.

The inspection of the property for a valuation should include a 'head and shoulders' viewing of the roof space, but it is not necessary to actually physically enter the roof space. Since the insurance risk is very often assessed as a result of this inspection, any significant factors affecting risk (such as the close proximity of trees on clay subsoils, any fire hazards and any evidence of subsidence) should be reported upon.

Some lenders are moving away from the formal mortgage valuation report and are placing more emphasis upon the borrower's ability to repay the loan. Such companies are relying upon a 'drive-past' or 'desktop' valuation (without the surveyor inspecting the interior or any part of the property), just to ascertain whether the proposed purchase price is in the correct price bracket. This is a trend that may well become more prevalent in the future.

2.2.2 Property purchase survey and valuation

This is an intermediate survey between the valuation inspection described above and the building survey (see section 2.2.3 below); it advises on value as well as giving factual information on significant aspects of the condition of the dwelling. The survey is carried out under standard conditions of engagement prepared by the professional organisation of which the surveyor is a member. The report is prepared to a standard format approved by the professional organisation. An example of this type of survey is the Homebuyer Survey and Valuation originally introduced by The Royal Institution of Chartered Surveyors (RICS) in 1981.

This intermediate type of survey is usually described as an 'economy' service in which the client accepts that not every defect will be reported upon, but the surveyor is under a duty to report on the essential matters that are likely to affect the value of the property. Many more of this type of survey are carried out annually than are building surveys, but the surveyor should be aware that the level of liability is similar so that the inspection needs to be just as thorough. In carrying out the inspection the surveyor is required to carry a ladder capable of inspecting roofs 3.0 m high, but is not expected to raise fixed floorboards or lift fitted carpets. Those areas of the property that are accessible and which can be inspected safely should be reported upon, and roof spaces should be inspected. However, where the dwelling is a flat only those roof spaces that have direct access from the flat should be inspected. The common parts (that is, entrance hall, staircase and landing) leading to the flat should also be inspected. The services would normally be inspected and commented upon but not tested.

When the latest version of the RICS Homebuyer Survey was introduced in 1998, its use was for the first time included as a practice statement in the so-called 'Red Book' that governs all valuation services provided by chartered surveyors. This economy survey was never designed for large or old dwellings or for houses requiring extensive refurbishment, and for such properties the building survey described below would be a more appropriate service for the surveyor to offer.

2.2.3 Building survey

The building survey is an investigation and assessment of the construction and condition of a building, and does not always include advice upon value. This type of survey was originally called a 'structural survey'. The CIC document referred to earlier recommends that any survey carried out by a structural engineer should be referred to as an *inspection, appraisal, investigation* or *assessment* rather than as a survey. The principal reason for this shift in thinking is that the building survey involves rather more than an investigation and assessment of the structure as it is also concerned with the fabric, finishes, grounds and services. The services would normally only be inspected, and would be tested only if the client specifically required this extension to the normal service. Where of course the surveyor is suspicious of the condition of the services following inspection it would be appropriate to recommend that they be tested.

The main differences between the building survey inspection and that required for the intermediate survey are that fixed floorboards should normally be raised at each floor level, and secured duct covers should be opened up where this can be achieved without causing damage or without expending excessive time. Apart from these relatively minor differences the inspection for both types of survey should be of a similar level of detail.

As a general guide the time taken to carry out the inspection for a building survey of say a three-bedroom, semi-detached house would be 3 hours (compared with 2 hours for the intermediate survey and about 30 or 45 minutes for a valuation inspection). The fees vary from region to region to reflect the different property market conditions, but the fee for a building survey would be about three times that for a valuation, and the fee for an intermediate inspection would be about double that for a valuation.

2.3   Changes in home selling

Following an extensive review of the home-selling process in England and Wales in 1999 the Government consulted upon proposals aimed at speeding up the entire process. Following a pilot study in the Bristol area it originally announced that it intended to bring forward legislation so that by 2003 the proposed changes would be mandatory, although it hoped that the changes would also be implemented on a voluntary basis before then. The biggest change is the more equal balancing of the cost of the house-selling process. This will involve the house seller in the preparation of an information pack before the house is placed on the market: it will be a criminal offence for the seller and, where appropriate, the seller's estate agent to offer for sale any dwelling for which an information pack has not been prepared.

The information pack will contain an up-to-date local authority search, any guarantee documents (for example for woodworm remedial treatment), and a 'report upon condition'. It is anticipated that the condition report will be similar to the intermediate form of survey discussed above. The RICS Homebuyer Survey and Valuation was used for the properties that were included in the Bristol pilot studies. The main problem that this aspect of the proposed legislation seeks to address is that currently the buyer often has to renegotiate the purchase price following receipt of the survey report. It is at this stage that many transactions stall or even break down completely. If the buyer has read the survey report before making an offer then this hurdle will not need to be jumped in future.

Thus these fundamental changes will move the responsibility for commissioning the survey report from the buyer to the seller, and every property that is placed on the market will have to be surveyed. This will greatly increase the number of surveys carried out, and it has been estimated that between 2,500 and 4,500 additional surveyors will be required throughout England and Wales to cope with this increased workload. Of course in some instances the prospective buyers may wish to commission a more detailed survey (for example a building survey), and some buyers may not feel confident about the neutrality or reliability of a report prepared by a surveyor appointed by the seller. There will also have to be changes in the legal arrangements to enable both the seller and the eventual buyer of the property to take action against the surveyor in the event of professional negligence.

The other types of inspection described in the CIC definitions document are now considered briefly.

2.4   Elemental or specialist investigation

This will be required where concern exists over specific parts of, or defects in, a building. Examples of this specialist work are a detailed study of movement, cracking, bulging, timber decay, dampness, or the testing of the electrical wiring. Such an inspection may arise as a result of one of the inspections already discussed, if the surveyor has recommended that further investigation is necessary. The scope of this type of investigation will be specific to each individual job and may involve an inspection by one or more professionals and possibly input from trade specialists.

2.5   Investigation prior to alteration

This may be required prior to the extension or alteration of an existing building. Subject to the necessary authority being obtained from the building owner, it may involve opening up, measuring, calculations to check the adequacy of structural and service elements, and detailed tests. This investigation can be more detailed than that required for a building survey and is likely to involve the services of a number of specialists.

2.6   Reinstatement cost assessment for insurance

This service is very often carried out as part of the three main domestic surveys described above but can of course be provided independently, and will also be carried out for commercial buildings. It involves the measurement of the gross external floor area of the building and the application of an appropriate unit rate (usually £ per square metre) in order to estimate the cost of demolition and reconstruction costs including all fees. This cost will have no direct relationship to the market value of the property, and indeed for a large building located in a modestly priced area it can be several times greater than the market value. Usually a reinstatement cost assessment will be made by reference to figures published by The Royal Institution of Chartered Surveyors/Building Cost Information Service (RICS/BCIS). However, for domestic properties the Association of British Insurers also produces useful summary tables of unit rates. Where the building is non-standard or has particularly valuable features (for example where the building is listed) it may be possible to assess reconstruction costs only by preparing approximate building quantities and costing them. In such instances the fee quoted for this service would need to reflect the work required.

2.7 Stock condition survey

This will be commissioned to assess the state of repair or condition of an organisation's current building stock in connection with the preparation of a planned preventive maintenance programme. Perhaps the most common client for such a service would be a public-sector housing landlord, but any owner of large numbers of buildings could commission this service. Nowadays most large property owners maintain quite sophisticated computerised databases of their portfolios, and sometimes surveyors carrying out stock condition inspections are required to enter data directly into hand-held computers on site.

2.8 Schedule of condition

This records the condition of a building at a particular time, and is often supported by photographs, sketches and drawings. The report should be in sufficient detail for any subsequent defects or items of disrepair to be readily identified. The two most common occasions that require the preparation of schedules of condition are at the beginning of a lease and prior to the commencement of adjacent construction or engineering work. In the first instance it is usually the tenant who will be responsible for upkeep of the building who wishes to have a record of the condition when his or her liability commenced. In the second scenario the owner of the property may wish to make a claim if any damage arises from the building or engineering works but will need to have an agreed record of the condition before any work commences. It is usual for a schedule of condition to have a tabular format, and in some respects the preparation of such a schedule is less onerous than for example the carrying out of a building survey. If there are defects present it is sufficient merely to record the precise extent of these (for example by sketching any cracks to show their width and length) rather than analyse why the defects have occurred.

2.9 Schedule of dilapidations

A schedule of dilapidations is required to identify the items of disrepair of tenanted property under the terms of a lease. It may be prepared for service on the landlord or tenant, depending on their respective repairing obligations under the lease. A schedule may be terminal (served at the end of the lease) or interim (served where the lease has three or more years to run). The purpose of the interim schedule is to point out the repairs that the tenant is required to carry out to fulfil his or her obligations under the lease, and it is usually far less detailed than a terminal schedule. Both types of schedule are usually produced in tabular form, and in the later stages of the process the schedule will need to be priced to quantify the dilapidations. It is usual for a surveyor to be appointed by both the tenant and the landlord and for the two surveyors to agree the extent and cost of work required. Where agreement cannot be reached, the matter will proceed to litigation.

2.10 Measured survey

As discussed in Chapter 1 a measured (or dimensional) survey involves taking measurements of a building and/or site in order to prepare accurate drawings to scale, usually prior to the design of alteration or extension works. Such a survey may include taking levels.

2.11 Inspection of buildings under construction

The final inspection defined by the CIC is the inspection of buildings under construction. Such inspections are required for a variety of reasons, and the exact purpose will dictate the frequency and scope of the inspection and the reporting format. Examples of this type of inspection are the statutory inspections required under the Building Regulations and certification inspections under building contracts. A particularly common service that falls under this category is the inspection to certify the construction of a new dwelling. Inspections of this type may be carried out by an employee of the National House Building Council or by an independent architect or surveyor. Certification that the construction of a house is satisfactory is usually a prerequisite for obtaining mortgage funding to purchase a new house. In this case the surveyor makes approximately 10 inspections at predetermined stages (from the inspection of the foundation trenches through until completion) and certifies that the work is in accordance with the approved drawings and that it complies with good practice.

There are a number of other types of survey that are not specifically mentioned in the CIC document; these are considered below.

2.12 Commercial properties

Most of the inspections described above are equally applicable to commercial property as they are to residential buildings. The possible exception is the property purchase survey and valuation that was specifically introduced for modest-sized domestic property. The estimation of rental values for commercial property is also a rather specialist activity and is usually carried out by a valuation surveyor.

The commercial building surveyor requires an awareness of a broader range of legislation than the surveyor confining him or herself to domestic property. A working knowledge of the Fire Precautions Act and Offices, Shops and Railways Premises Act, for example, is required.

The potential costs of professional negligence (see Chapter 3) can be very much higher for commercial property than for residential buildings, however. This is because the consequent loss claims could be so much greater. If for example a surveyor failed to notice roof defects of a warehouse where expensive goods were being stored, the costs of replacing the damaged goods could be very much higher than the cost of re-roofing.

2.13 Ecclesiastical inspections

The survey of churches is a specialist activity, and indeed some architects and surveyors specialise in this work to the exclusion of all other professional activities. The Church of England maintenance programme is formalised, and has as its basis a quinquennial review of all churches. Church buildings are inspected every five years, and a programme of maintenance, repair and improvement works is drawn up for the period up to the next review. Other denominations, for example Roman Catholics and Methodists, often have a regular inspection programme. In this sense this inspection could come under the earlier heading of a stock condition survey. However, the stock is rather specialised, and traditionally the architect or surveyor responsible for a particular church has maintained a long-term relationship with the building.

2.14 Historic buildings

Just as some professionals specialise in ecclesiastical work so others confine their activities to historic buildings. The conservation profession has become increasingly important in the last decade or so, and many architects, engineers and surveyors specialise in this form of work. The Society for the Protection of Ancient Buildings (SPAB) has been at the forefront of a rethink of how to conserve our built heritage, and offers advice to professionals and building owners on both the principles and the practice of conservation. SPAB is particularly keen to promote detailed consideration by prospective purchasers of historic buildings. Its 'look before you leap' campaign has stressed the importance of clients taking professional advice before they purchase so that they do not do irreversible damage to a building in their haste to adapt it to their needs. Rather SPAB advocates that historic property owners should adapt themselves to the existing building instead of the other way round. SPAB has recently consulted on a standard format for a survey report for historic buildings, and it is likely that this format will be in use before too long.

2.15 Summary

Before 1997 there was much confusion in the minds of clients, and sometimes in the minds of their professional advisers, over the titles given to the various types of survey. The Construction Industry Council document *Definitions of Inspections and Surveys of Buildings* has done much to remedy this situation, although it is likely that some members of the built environment professions will continue to use 'outlawed' titles such as 'structural survey' for some time to come. The three most common inspections of residential property are the valuation, the property purchase survey and valuation, and the building survey. The intermediate survey is likely to form the basis of the 'condition report' to be included in an information pack supplied by sellers to prospective buyers of all residential property in England and Wales in the future. The other types of survey that are appropriate for both residential and commercial property have been considered in this chapter. In the next chapter the preliminary steps that the surveyor needs to take before carrying out the inspection are discussed.

Note

1 CIC *Definitions of Inspections and Surveys of Buildings* (Construction Industry Council, London, 1997).

3 Preliminary steps

3.1 Introduction

This chapter is concerned with the essential matters that the surveyor needs to attend to before leaving the office to carry out the survey. Professional indemnity insurers advise that there are more problems with this aspect of surveying work than with any other. It is simply not possible to rush off and carry out a survey immediately one receives the telephone instructions to do so; there are a number of preliminary steps that are required to clarify exactly what the client requires and how the service will be provided. If nothing else there are a number of legal niceties that need to be attended to before the survey is undertaken.

3.2 Taking instructions

Many commissions initially come via the telephone, but it is not always the client at the other end of the line. It may be that a solicitor or licensed conveyancer contacts the surveyor to arrange the survey. Other professionals who may recommend or refer clients to surveyors are estate agents, accountants, bank managers and building society managers. The surveyor must ensure, however, that the instructions are taken directly from the client, and this will mean obtaining contact details from the referrer so that the client can be approached directly, probably initially by telephone.

The first thing to be ascertained is which of the wide variety of surveys described in Chapter 2 the client requires. Let us assume for the purpose of this discussion that the client requires a building survey of a residential property and that the surveyor has telephoned the client as a result of a referral from the client's solicitor. The surveyor should ascertain basic details of the property: type (house or flat); whether detached, semi-detached or terraced; approximate age; size (number of storeys, number of rooms); and location. This information should enable the surveyor to quote a fee, which is what the client will be particularly interested in. The surveyor should offer preliminary advice on the suitability of the type of survey required. For example, if the client were to request a Homebuyer Survey of a large, old or dilapidated dwelling the surveyor would have to advise that such a service would be inappropriate.

The client may require the services of other specialists such as an electrician or a timber and damp-proof contractor, and the surveyor should indicate the availability, suitability and likely cost of such inspections (see Chapter 4 for more about other consultants). Once the client has agreed to pay the amount quoted by the surveyor it is necessary for the client to be sent and to agree the conditions of engagement.

3.3   Conditions of engagement

There have been instances where clients have successfully sued surveyors on the basis that they were expecting a full building survey but the surveyor had provided only an inspection and valuation. In order to avoid this possible problem, precise details of the service to be provided need to be agreed in writing by both parties before the survey is undertaken: this is the main reason why a survey cannot be carried out immediately instructions are received. In the scenario outlined above the surveyor would deliver or post written conditions of engagement to the client. Most surveyors have standard conditions, and indeed if a Homebuyers Survey is to be provided then the standard RICS conditions of engagement would be used. It is important for conditions of engagement to spell out in great detail what will be undertaken during the inspection and reporting stages of the survey and – perhaps more importantly – what will *not* be provided.

Although it may be sufficient for the surveyor merely to notify the conditions of engagement to the client in order to avoid any ambiguity at a later date, it is preferable to have some mechanism for the client to agree in writing that he or she has read the conditions and agrees to them. Again, most firms have a standard form that the client needs to sign and return to the surveyor. Once the surveyor has received the signed form it is safe to carry out the survey. Given that the client may be based a considerable distance from the surveyor it is usually several days before this essential correspondence can be completed by post. Of course the fax machine has enabled it to be completed within a shorter timescale. Service of documents by fax is now recognised by the Civil Procedure Rules: Rule 6.2(1)(e). See also *Hastie and Jenkerson v McMahon.*[1]

The Consumers Association has been very critical of some surveyors' written conditions of engagement, in that it believes they are over-long and over-complicated. Indeed it was criticism from the Association that prompted the RICS to reduce significantly the length and complexity of the standard conditions of engagement for the Homebuyers Survey and Valuation. Most surveyors would be well advised to follow the example of the RICS in this regard.

3.4   Fees

Since the professional bodies representing property and construction professionals abolished mandatory fee scales in the 1980s it is no longer possible for the RIBA or the RICS to publish fee scales. Indeed the Office of Fair Trading has also outlawed *recommended* fee scales for such services. Of course it is local competition that determines the level of survey fees in any particular locality. If in doubt as to what the market will bear it is probably best to telephone a few surveyors in the guise of a potential client and to be quoted fees for carrying out various types of survey.

When a mortgage applicant instructs a building society or bank valuer it is usual for the fee to be collected in advance. As a result of this practice many surveyors have adopted similar arrangements for the collection of survey fees prior to undertaking the survey. Solicitors and estate agents, two of the other professionals involved in the house-buying and selling process, have adopted procedures that ensure that they collect payment of their fees before the legal transaction is completed. It is not surprising therefore that most surveyors attempt to ensure that there is some certainty of their receiving payment. At one time the author practised in an area of the UK that is popular with holidaymakers and where property values were relatively low. It was quite common for holidaymakers to fall in love with the area during a summer visit and decide to purchase a second home. If the fee was not collected in advance then it was sometimes difficult to obtain payment; some clients would rapidly go off the idea of purchasing the property once they had returned home.

3.5 Professional indemnity insurance

Evidence from professional indemnity insurers suggests that survey and valuation work is one of the highest-risk activities undertaken by property and construction professionals. Over the last 20 years or so the incidence and value of claims have been substantially higher than for other property activities such as estate agency and architecture. Of course if a client purchases a property with defects of which he or she was not aware after reading a survey report it is only natural that said client will seek financial recompense from the surveyor. It is therefore essential that the surveyor report all *relevant* defects: what is considered relevant in any given situation will depend upon the type of survey carried out.

In an increasingly litigious and consumer-oriented society the definition of what constitutes professional negligence seems to have narrowed in the popular mind to that of making any mistake whatsoever. The legal liability that any professional incurs in carrying out a professional service for a client stems from common law, and in particular from the tort of negligence. The professional's primary responsibility is to perform the service with reasonable skill and care. Failure to meet this standard, by omission or act, is likely to be deemed professional negligence.

For a claim to succeed in negligence there must be a breach of a duty of care, and damage must result from the breach. Very often the only defence a professional has against a claim for negligence is that the subject dealt with is not generally known to the profession: this is called the *state of art* defence.

The professional institutions are anxious that their members' clients should not be disadvantaged by the negligent acts of their members, and many have a system of compulsory professional indemnity insurance. Some (for example the Law Society) act as the insurer of last resort for their members. The RICS has regulations that stipulate minimum levels of cover and maximum levels of excesses. Chartered surveyors who cannot obtain insurance that complies with the requirements of these regulations are effectively prohibited from practising their profession.

Professional indemnity insurance is on a 'claims made' basis. This means that it is necessary for the surveyor to have insurance *at the time that a claim is made*. Therefore it is necessary for the surveyor to maintain what is known as *run-off cover* on retirement. The minimum duration of such cover is six years, but some authorities recommend that a longer period be adopted since a claim can be brought in tort within three years of the discovery of a defect, and the cut-off point is 15 years or – in some instances – even longer.

Many construction professionals find the cost of insurance to be prohibitively expensive, and because the uninsured excesses for certain types of work are so high, a successful claim by a client can severely affect the financial standing of a professional. It is not uncommon for a surveyor to have to find the first £5,000 or £10,000 of any claim from his or her own pocket.

In the interests of members' clients, some professional organisations are prepared to legislate in areas beyond those in which even the courts are prepared to act. The RICS has introduced increased disciplinary powers that enable it to impose financial penalties of up to £5,000 upon defaulting members. The RICS imposes a requirement upon chartered surveying firms to establish a complaints-handling procedure. In addition lay representation is included on disciplinary boards.

The considerable increase in the incidence of professional indemnity claims means that it is highly unlikely that any surveyor will be in the happy situation of never having a claim made against them during their career. It is very important therefore to be aware of the correct procedure to follow in the unfortunate eventuality of a claim being made. Of course each insurance policy will be slightly different, and so the surveyor should check the policy before taking any action, but the following general comments are offered for guidance.

Most policies require the insurer to be notified in the event of a claim arising. Thus even if the surveyor believes that the value of a claim is likely to fall within the uninsured excess in the policy it is still necessary to notify the insurer. The reason for this is that small claims often have a nasty habit of developing into bigger claims – particularly when the lawyers get involved. Most policies stipulate that the insured should never admit liability even if they believe that they have been negligent. Being accused of negligence can of course be a traumatic experience, and if possible it is always better for another surveyor to deal with the complaint. Of course where the surveyor is a sole principal this is not possible.

If the surveyor is unfortunate enough to have a claim that proceeds to court then it is the insurer who will decide when or if the claim should be settled. Thus a surveyor may believe that he or she has not been negligent but the insurer, wary of incurring the enormous costs that a court case will incur, may insist on settling – even though this means that the poor surveyor is then liable for the uninsured excess. This can be overcome to some extent by having a 'QC' clause in the policy.[2]

The topics of professional negligence and professional indemnity insurance are inherently rather depressing. However, the wise surveyor will ensure that the subjects are at the forefront of their mind when carrying out any service for a client – particularly what seems to be the risky business of a building or other survey.

3.6   Visit to site

When quoting a fee for the work as outlined in section 3.2 above the surveyor may decide with a particularly unusual property that it is not possible to do this without first visiting the site. This is an eminently sensible idea, as it is obviously better to discover something that is likely to affect the cost of providing the service before a fee has been quoted rather than after. The author recalls arriving at a very large residential home just prior to carrying out a full building survey only to discover that it was not a residential home for the elderly but a home for the mentally ill. Thus what he anticipated would take a couple of days to inspect actually took four days, mainly as a result of the home's residents locking him in a number of rooms and stealing his ladder while surveying roof spaces. Unfortunately the residents perceived the surveyor's presence as a threat to their continued enjoyment of the property and were determined to make his life as difficult as possible. A quick visit to the property beforehand would have at least prepared the surveyor for this unusual experience.

Provided the property is within reasonable travelling distance of the surveyor's office a preliminary visit to site is always a good idea even where the conditions of engagement have been finalised. The initial 15–30 minutes on site when carrying out a survey are very often spent in familiarising oneself with the layout of the site and buildings. An initial visit prepares the surveyor in advance, reducing this familiarisation time, and may inform him or her as to specialist equipment or consultants required to carry out the inspection.

3.7 Initial research

For a building of non-straightforward construction a preliminary visit may well inform the surveyor that it would be an advantage to obtain the original or as-built drawings. Particularly in a commercial building it is not always possible to determine exact details of the construction without some drawings to assist.

The usual rider needs to be added here that the building may not have been constructed exactly as originally designed. The author is aware of cases where even drawings marked 'as built' differed significantly in detail from what was actually constructed on site. Nevertheless, drawings can sometimes be a useful source of information. A visit to the local authority building control office can often prove fruitful in this respect. Even if the drawings cannot be inspected in detail in the council offices it will usually be possible to discover who the original architect was. It will normally be possible to obtain copies of the drawings from the original architect – provided of course that the building is reasonably modern. Other sources of information are discussed in Chapter 5.

3.8 Surveying safely

In preparing for the survey it is necessary to consider the safety of all personnel involved in the exercise. Advice about the safe use of surveying equipment and other safety matters is contained in the RICS publication *Surveying Safely: A Personal Commitment.*[3]

3.9 Summary

There are a number of essential activities that need to be undertaken before carrying out a survey. Detailed instructions need to be taken, and these should be confirmed in writing, with preferably the client's written acceptance obtained. Many surveyors take this opportunity to obtain advance payment of their fees. It is essential that professional indemnity insurance be in place for what, statistics from insurers suggest, is a riskier service than general architectural work or estate agency. Provided it is practical, a preliminary site visit can save time during the early part of the actual survey and can inform the surveyor on what initial research is required (see Chapter 5) and what specialist equipment and consultants may be needed. In the next chapter the services that these other consultants can provide to the surveyor and the client are discussed.

Notes

1 *Hastie and Jenkerson v McMahon, The Times,* 3 April 1990.
2 A QC clause in a professional indemnity insurance policy provides that the insured person can insist that a claim be defended if Queen's Counsel advises that there is a valid defence.
3 RICS *Surveying Safely: A Personal Commitment* (The Royal Institution of Chartered Surveyors, London, 1991).

4   Specialists

4.1   The surveyor's core knowledge

It is an essential characteristic of a professional that they are aware of the boundaries of their own competence and know when to seek advice from, or refer their client to, a specialist. General practice doctors refer their patients to a specialist when confronted with acute symptoms they are not sure of; the solicitor refers the client to the appropriate barrister; and so on. As the world becomes increasingly complicated it is impossible for a practitioner in any professional field to have all the knowledge and experience required to be able to advise every client about every problem in a particular area of expertise.

This discussion leads us to ask the question: What is the professional's core knowledge? Certainly in the case of the medical GP there is widespread understanding of what that core knowledge is: a general knowledge of anatomy and physiology, and an ability to diagnose the symptoms that a patient presents. When one asks the same question about a surveyor the answer depends upon what type of surveyor we are considering. A valuation surveyor's core knowledge is an awareness of local property markets – be they residential or commercial – but the surveyor who is principally concerned with assessing condition needs other knowledge. The main requirement is a thorough understanding of construction technology. Unless the surveyor is completely aware of how the building being inspected has been (or perhaps more importantly should have been) constructed he or she will not be in a position to detect defects. Of course this knowledge also has a time dimension in that the building being inspected may have been erected at any time over the last thousand years. Not all surveyors would feel confident in inspecting a very old building, and in such situations the surveyor would no doubt refer the client to a surveyor who specialised in historic buildings. The age of the properties that a surveyor is likely to inspect will obviously depend upon the location of the surveying practice. A surveyor working in the centre of say Oxford is likely to be inspecting many more older buildings than a surveyor practising in Milton Keynes.

This introduces the question of the size of the geographical area over which a particular surveyor should be prepared to undertake inspections. There are certain building types that are peculiar to a particular region. For example, clay lump is limited largely to areas of East Anglia (although there are similar earth buildings with different names in other parts of the UK). Early timber-framed buildings are constructed in different ways in different parts of the country. Building terminology also varies from region to region. If a surveyor is to have an awareness of the geology and how this affects the potential for foundation failure in a particular locality it is likely that he or she will restrict themselves to working in a fairly limited geographical area. Of course the density of development also needs to be considered in this context. A surveyor may well be able to make a living by operating exclusively in a particular urban location, whereas a surveyor working in a rural setting will have to travel much wider in order for the workload to be economically viable.

So far we have said that surveyors need to have knowledge of building construction and that this knowledge should be in the context of the particular locality in which they accept instructions. Other essential requirements are an awareness of how buildings fail, how they deteriorate over time, and how they can be returned to satisfactory condition after they have failed or deteriorated. For a simple domestic building situated in the locality in which an experienced surveyor works it is possible that the surveyor will possess the entire knowledge necessary to carry out a complete and thorough survey of the property. Such instances will be in the minority, and in most situations it will be necessary to call upon the services of specialists if a complete service is to be provided to the client. Very often it is for the surveyor concerned to make the decision about when it is necessary to refer to or call upon a specialist. Failure in this respect could have dire consequences. The employment of specialists needs to be considered from two viewpoints – at the time of accepting instructions and when reporting to the client. However, before discussing this aspect we shall consider the various types of specialist who may be employed.

4.2   Other professionals

The specialists likely to be called in to assist the surveyor will either be fellow professionals or contractors or tradesmen. We shall first consider the other consultants likely to be involved, commencing with the *structural engineer*. The client is paying for a 'survey' and will be less than impressed if the surveyor employs another consultant to advise upon simple movement of a traditional building such as settlement or subsidence. The diagnosis and rectification of such defects are part of the 'core knowledge' referred to above. However, there will undoubtedly be instances where the structural engineer's expertise will be required. Say for example a chimney-breast has been removed within the building but remains within a roof space. In many such situations it is possible to say that the method of support is inadequate (where for example the support is off the slender ceiling joists). In others situations, however, the decision is more finely balanced, for example where a large-section timber has been used. Some surveyors would be confident in checking by calculation whether the particular section used was adequate; many more, however, would prefer to call on the services of an engineer to verify the method of support. Other situations that may demand the services of a structural engineer are where excessive deflection of components requires that they be checked by calculation or where specialised foundations are involved.

An *acoustic engineer* may be required where there is doubt about the soundproofing of a separating or party wall, or where the acoustic performance of a special space such as an auditorium or meeting hall requires assessing. Such services are likely to be required only in exceptional circumstances and then only for commercial buildings. For specialist sanitary and drainage installations of commercial buildings it is possible that the services of a *civil engineer* will be required but in smaller, domestic-scale buildings it is more likely that a general builder or specialist tradesman will be employed to undertake drainage inspections and tests. Similarly in a particularly complicated commercial building it is likely that *building services engineers* will be employed to inspect and report upon the service installations. For a dwelling, however, a heating engineer or plumber may be engaged to survey the heating and domestic hot and cold water installations. Where a specialist is not employed then the surveyor will be expected to report on the type, age and condition of the plumbing installations.

4.3   Employing contractors

There are occasions when it is impossible to determine the full extent of a method of construction or defect without opening up the structure. Provided the owner of the property is willing for such opening up to take place the surveyor will probably wish to engage a general building contractor to undertake the necessary opening up and if necessary the subsequent reinstatement work. There will no doubt be some survey work, particularly where large-scale refurbishment or alteration is planned, where the work carried out by a general contractor will be extensive. However, it is most unlikely that the seller of a pristine dwelling would be willing to allow any opening up whatsoever.

When inspecting drainage installations the surveyor is expected to locate and identify inspection chambers and also to raise covers to determine the likelihood of any problems. The presence of blockages and tree roots will obviously give cause for concern, and the condition of the inspection chambers is a guide to the general condition of the installation. It can be difficult to raise corroded iron or steel covers, and the surveyor will need to carry a variety of implements for this task (see Chapter 6). Sometimes the surveyor will need to engage a contractor to lift a particularly tight-fitting cover, and it may be necessary to break and replace a cover in some extreme situations.

As mentioned above, a general contractor may be the most appropriate person to undertake drain testing, although there are specialist contractors who may be able to undertake this work more competitively. Traditionally, drain runs have been pressure-tested by filling them with water or air. Smoke testing is appropriate for drains above ground, and the use of dyes enables drain runs to be traced. New drains are always subjected to a water pressure test as part of the Building Regulations compliance process. However, pressure tests can damage old drains, particularly those with weak joints, and the permission of the owner of the property should always be obtained before applying a water or air test to any drain. Some surveyors carry their own drain-testing equipment (see Chapter 6) and are prepared to apply their own tests. However, this is really appropriate only for drainage layouts of limited size. Where the installation is extensive it would take several hours to apply water or air tests, and this is hardly the most economical use of the surveyor's time.

Applying a pressure test to a drain run will reveal whether or not the drain is watertight, but it will not identify where the leak is occurring. This fact, together with the risk of damaging existing drains, is the main reason why pressure testing is increasingly being replaced by the use of closed-circuit television (CCTV) surveys. Specialist contractors use specially adapted drain rods to insert a small video camera along the full length of the drain. The resulting survey consists of a video cassette that will identify exactly where the defect is located. The only disadvantage is that the extent of any leakage is not revealed by a CCTV inspection. As a result of increasing competition the costs of CCTV surveys of drainage installations have fallen significantly since they were first introduced.

The electrical installation of a building is another area in which the surveyor may require specialist advice. As we shall see in Chapter 9, it is necessary as a minimum for the surveyor to identify the type of mains supply, location and type of meters and consumer units, and the type and approximate age of the wiring and fittings. Earthing arrangements may also need to be commented on. Where it is obvious from the age of the wiring and fittings that extensive rewiring works are necessary it is appropriate for the surveyor to advise so and to recommend that competitive quotations be obtained. There is more of a problem when the installation appears to have modern wiring and fittings: how far should the surveyor inspect in this situation? What is required of the surveyor is an inspection; there is no requirement for the surveyor to *test* the installation.

The Institution of Electrical Engineers (IEE) Regulations do not have the same statutory force as for example the Building Regulations, but the mains service provider will normally require certification that a new installation complies with the IEE Regulations before connecting the property to the mains supply. The Regulations also state that an installation should be tested every five years. It would therefore be appropriate in the circumstances suggested above to recommend to a purchaser that a copy of the latest certificate be obtained. Of course where a client specifically requests that an electrical test be carried out then the surveyor is able to pass on his or her liability in respect of the electrical installation to the electrician engaged to provide this service.

At the heart of the core knowledge expected of the surveyor is the ability to detect, categorise and recommend remedial work for damp problems and fungal attack and insect infestation in timber. As a general rule, therefore, specialist advice should therefore only be sought in connection with the likely cost of remedial works. Specialist damp and timber treatment companies are in business to sell their remedial work. Some of these firms are reputable but many are not – as evidenced by several high-profile cases reported in the media recently. There are very few damp and timber treatment consultants who exist only to offer advice, and such consultants would of course charge fees for such advice.

The problem with diagnosis of dampness problems is that it is not always possible to distinguish accurately between penetrating or rising dampness and condensation. Detailed environmental monitoring of internal ambient temperature and absolute/relative humidity is sometimes necessary over several weeks or even months to be absolutely certain as to the cause of some dampness problems. Such monitoring is beyond the scope of most surveys, but it would be appropriate to recommend it where the surveyor is not able to diagnose a particular dampness problem from a simple visual inspection and the use of a moisture meter. Similarly it is not always easy to distinguish between dry rot and wet rot, although dry rot remedial works are very much more expensive. Accurate diagnosis is therefore of considerable importance, and this may involve some opening up of the structure to search for the tell-tale signs of dry rot (see Chapter 8). The surveyor is expected to identify whether insect infestation is active or not, and to distinguish between the various types of insect. A specialist contractor should be consulted regarding the estimated cost of remedial work. More environmentally friendly solutions to timber infestation are sought nowadays. As with all cases where estimates are sought for clients more than one price should be obtained.

4.4   Engagement of specialists

At the time of taking instructions from the client the appointment of specialists should be considered. The client may have firm ideas about the level of service they require, and they may request that drainage and electrical tests be included from the beginning. In other situations the surveyor may be able to recommend the appointment of a particular specialist after discussing the matter with the client over the telephone. Where for example the surveyor is aware that most properties in a particular location have pitch fibre drains it is likely that a specialist drainage survey will be recommended from the outset. In such situations it is always best for the client to appoint the specialist contractor or consultant directly. Such an arrangement has two advantages: the specialist will be responsible for collecting their fee directly from the client, and if there is subsequently any dispute between the parties the surveyor does not need to become involved in the disagreement.

In many situations the surveyor will not know that a specialist is required until actually carrying out the survey. In such situations it would be appropriate to recommend in the report that the client engage the services of the specialist. However, it is always best to advise the client of the need for a specialist at the earliest opportunity. A client is unlikely to be impressed, after waiting some time for a survey report to arrive, to read it only to discover that it is merely a list of specialists to be consulted. It was this issue that the Consumers' Association was concerned about and which persuaded the RICS to revise its Homebuyers Survey (many commentators believe that the changes introduced in 1998 have made little improvement in this regard). Surveyors must not merely hide behind the skirts of a string of specialists recommended to inspect the property but must give their own professional opinion wherever possible. The surveyor has to balance the need not to overstep the boundaries of competence against the need to do what the client is actually paying for – to offer a professional opinion. By all means recommend that specialists provide estimates of the cost of remedial work but do not recommend that others provide the actual service that the client expects from the surveyor.

4.5   Which specialists are being used?

Table 4.1 gives an indication of the type of work currently being referred to specialists by surveyors, in terms of the percentages of a recent sample of 143 UK building surveyors referring the use of surveying equipment. The research project is described in more detail in Chapter 6.

Table 4.1 Percentages of surveyors referring use of equipment

Equipment	Percentage referring (n = 143)
Recording/viewing	
Thermal image camera	11.9
Digital camera	0.7
Video camera	1.4
35 mm camera	0.7
Endoscope	25.9

Table 4.1 Percentages of surveyors referring use of equipment – *continued*

Equipment	Percentage referring (*n* = 143)
Hand lens	0
Binoculars	0
Inspection mirror	0
Compass	0
Battery torch	0
Electric survey lighting	0.7
Dictaphone	0
Microscope	7.0
Image analysis software	3.5
PC with word processing or spreadsheet	0.7
PC with diagnostic software	0.7
Measurement	
Steel tape	0
Fabric tape	0
Electronic measure	0.7
Tread-wheel	4.9
Crack width measurer	3.5
Movement measurer	8.4
Level	10.5
Plumb-line etc.	2.1
Environmental	
Thermometer	4.2
Hygrometer	6.3
Anemometer	7.0
Carbon dioxide detector	14.0
Radon detector	15.4
Light meter	7.0
Noise meter	15.4
Moisture meter: pin probe	3.5
Moisture meter: surface	1.4
Moisture meter: other	9.1
Material detectors	
'Studmaster'	5.6
Metal detector	7.7

Table 4.1 Percentages of surveyors referring use of equipment – *continued*

Equipment	Percentage referring (*n* = 143)
Electrical testing	
Earth meter	37.8
Mains tester	37.1
Other tester	14.0
Drain testing	
CCTV	60.8
Smoke bomb	32.9
Fluid dye	31.5
Bung/balloon stopper	32.9
Metals	
Electronic paint gauge	19.6
Timber	
Integrity awl	6.3
'Sibert' integrity drill	7.7
Concrete/mortar	
Chemical analysis kit	32.9
ISAT permeability	13.3
Rebound hammer	19.6
Reinforcement cover meter	25.2
Radar survey	12.6
Ultrasonic pulse velocity kit	9.1
Plastics	
'Durometer'	4.9
Brick/stone	
Ultrasonic pulse velocity kit	6.3
Flat roofs	
Leak detector	19.6

The results of the survey are predictable: the most referred work is the use of an endoscope, electrical and drain testing, chemical analysis of concrete/mortar and the use of a reinforcement cover meter. About one-fifth of the sample also refer flat roof leak detection and electronic paint gauge measurement. As we discuss further in Chapters 6 and 9 there appears to be a slight trend towards following the US practice of the surveyor taking on more responsibility for testing services, but the results of this research confirm the traditional view that electrical and drain testing is currently the work most often referred to specialists.

4.6   Summary

The complexity of modern-day buildings makes it is unlikely that a surveyor will possess all the skills and knowledge needed to report on every aspect of a building. Therefore various specialists are likely to be employed, either initially by the surveyor, or by the client following recommendation by the surveyor. A survey of practitioners has revealed that the use of an endoscope, testing of services and testing of concrete are the most referred work.

Now that the surveyor has agreed the conditions of engagement with the client and has decided which specialists to call on for assistance, we are nearly ready to leave the office to undertake the inspection. However, before we do so we shall consider in the next chapter what information the surveyor can obtain about the property before visiting the site.

5   Sources of information

5.1   Introduction

We are nearly ready to commence our inspection of the property, but first we should spend a little time contemplating the possible types of information we are likely to require and the likely sources of that information. Most of the information that we need to process before writing the report will result from our physical inspection of the building, but there will undoubtedly be other information that the surveyor obtains from third parties, and it is necessary to consider how credible these additional sources of information are.

If for example we are told that a flat roof, to which access is particularly difficult, has been re-covered in the last 12 months, what should we do? Should we believe that source, or should we arrange for a longer ladder to inspect the roof? The answer to this question depends in part on just who the source of information is. If the source is the owner, who obviously has a considerable vested interest, then we should treat the source with suspicion; if however the source is a local authority officer then it is more likely that we can rely upon the information. Of course there is no better source than the evidence of one's own eyes, and if it is not too much trouble to get a longer ladder then this is what should be done.

In most cases the need for additional information will become apparent only after the inspection has been carried out, but in the following discussion it is possible that the information will be sought either before or after the inspection. Possible sources of information are considered below.

5.2   Existing owner

Anyone who has a vested interest in the disposal of the property should not be treated as a credible source of information. This obviously includes the existing owner of the property and the estate agent. However, the owner of the property (or the estate agent) is the one person with whom the surveyor is likely to come into contact. Where information is provided by the owner then this should wherever possible be verified by a third person. Where it is not possible to do this then the surveyor's report should clearly state that the evidence has been provided by the owner or the estate agent but that the surveyor is not able to confirm this information. Where the information is of a legal nature then of course the client should be advised to consult his or her solicitor or conveyancer. The above advice is likely to remain unchanged following the introduction of vendor surveys: the surveyor's liability will extend to those who eventually purchase the property, and the fact that initially the client and the owner are the same person means that the surveyor should still treat any information provided by the party wishing to dispose of the property with a good deal of scepticism.

One fact that owners of property are prone to exaggerate is the size of their plot. If the author had a pound for every property he had surveyed where the plot size was less than that indicated by the owner or estate agent he would be a very rich man.

5.3   Solicitor

One can normally assume that information provided by a solicitor or conveyancer is reliable. When inspecting leased property the surveyor must familiarise him or herself with the contents of the lease in so far as repairing obligations are concerned. On one occasion the author was sent the wrong lease for a dilapidations inspection but fortunately realised this before carrying out the inspection. One matter about which the client should always be referred to the solicitor is the liability for the repair of boundary walls and fences. The deeds will usually make reference to these, and information provided by owners and in particular by neighbours is often far from reliable.

5.4   Local authority

Valuable information about planning matters and hidden construction details can often be obtained from the relevant local authority department. Access to the original planning or building regulations drawings will often be provided by the local authority officers. Where the architect is still in practice it may well be possible to approach him or her to obtain copies of these drawings. The problem with relying upon the original drawings is that the building may not have been constructed as originally designed, but provided the building is not too old then the original architect may well be able to provide important information – either from files or from memory.

With old buildings, particularly those that are listed or are located in a conservation area, the local authority conservation officer is often a valuable source of information. Most conservation officers are enthusiastic about the buildings under their care and are happy to provide any information that they possess. The local historical society could also be consulted when any specific details are required. There may also be a local archive of film and photographic images that could provide specific information about the past façade of a particular building. Such detailed information may take time to trace, and its sourcing will often be beyond the scope of an initial purchase inspection. The information may however be useful for any follow-on design commission.

5.5   Other parties

The RICS guidance note for residential building surveys points out that:

> *Enquiry from people with past knowledge of the area can sometimes be very productive in identifying environmental factors and gaining an understanding of the development of the district and the history of the subject property (fire damage, flooding, subsidence damage, long period empty, etc.).*[1]

Sometimes this information will be volunteered by complete strangers when the surveyor is carrying out the inspection. Many neighbours seem keen to impart information about previous underpinning or Second World War bomb damage and so on. As the RICS guidance note suggests, this information can very often prove useful, often as a primer for discovering more detailed information. However, one should be wary about accepting the word of a complete stranger without obtaining any corroborating evidence.

5.6   Summary

The existing owner, solicitor, local authority officers, local record archives (the location of which varies from area to area) and indeed long-standing residents of an area can all provide valuable information to a surveyor. The surveyor should at all times consider how credible the source of the information is and indeed try to verify this information before passing it on to the client.

In the next chapter essential surveying equipment is considered.

Note

1 RICS *A Guidance Note for Surveyors: Building Surveys of Residential Property*, p 10 (The Royal Institution of Chartered Surveyors, London, 1996).

6   Essential surveying equipment

6.1   Introduction

The aids that the surveyor relies upon most when carrying out any form of
building inspection are eyesight, and knowledge and experience. However, there
will always be some physical equipment that the surveyor can use for assistance
both in recording information and in diagnosing defects. There is a minimum level
of equipment that must always be used, and this is specified in the various
published guidance notes to which a court of law would refer should there be any
suspicion of negligence. When undertaking residential surveys the guidance notes
are very explicit about what must be used.[1,2] For commercial and industrial
properties, however, the RICS guidance note is remarkably silent, stating only:

> *No list of equipment can be exhaustive nor can there be any suggestion that failure*
> *to carry items contained in a list of equipment may indicate a failure to carry out a*
> *survey adequately. It is also important to realise that the type of survey being*
> *undertaken will have a marked effect on the equipment likely to be required. The*
> *surveyor will make his decision based on the property being inspected and his*
> *instructions.*[3]

This suggests that those drafting this particular guidance note did not wish their
words to be used as a hostage to fortune, and therefore preferred to say nothing.

6.2   Equipment for residential surveys

The SAVA guidance note for homebuyer reports[2] states that the following
equipment must be used:

- suitable measuring tapes
- electronic moisture meter with spare batteries
- spirit level
- lifting equipment for drainage inspection chambers
- surveyor's ladder 3 m long
- powerful torch with spare batteries
- compass
- materials for recording site notes.

Reflecting the slightly more detailed inspection that should be undertaken for a
building survey the RICS guidance note[1] indicates that the following additional
equipment should be taken to the survey:

- claw hammer and bolster
- ladder of sufficient height to provide access to roofs and other areas not more than 3 m in height (note that this is a longer ladder than that required for the homebuyer survey)
- pocket probe for superficial testing of mortar, joinery, fracture depths, etc.
- binoculars or telescope
- hand mirror
- screwdriver
- plumb-line
- spirit level.

The guidance note says that optic probes, cover meters and similar specialist equipment are not normally included. The use to which this equipment is put is discussed in greater detail in Chapters 8, 9 and 10, which are concerned with the actual inspection. A compass is essential if surveying in an unfamiliar area on a cloudy day. Most surveyors prefer to describe the elevations of buildings by reference to their orientation, and this is the main use to which a compass is put. A plumb-line is essential for checking the verticality of walls, and a spirit level is obviously needed for checking whether floors etc. are horizontal.

Other items of equipment that the author has found useful on site include a spade to dig shallow trial holes, protective clothing to enable an inspection to be carried out whatever the conditions (overalls and wellington boots will usually suffice), a camera, drain-testing equipment, pocket lens magnifier, gauge for recording crack widths, and an electric lead lamp (in preference to a torch) to be used where mains electricity is available. Each surveyor will have individual preferences for the equipment to be taken to site, but it is important that the minimum level of equipment to fulfil the particular conditions of engagement and as recommended by the appropriate guidance note is always carried. It is no excuse to report to a client that a roof space has not been inspected because there were no ladders available to gain access.

There have been occasions when the author has been glad to have protective clothing available to inspect the *interior* of a property. Overalls and wellington boots are useful in repelling house fleas, which will continue to live on the carpets of vacant properties for some time after the other occupants of the house leave. Wellington boots also proved useful in repelling the unwanted attentions of geese on one occasion. A spade proved valuable once for digging for worms as fishing bait in the garden of a property that the author knew to be close to a particularly inviting lake that he intended to fish later in the day. The vendors arrived for a post-inspection briefing rather earlier than arranged, and this embarrassed surveyor mumbled something about checking the subsoil type before proceeding with his briefing.

6.3   Investigating current practice

The RICS Education Trust funded a research project[4] to ascertain whether the guidance notes referred to above are becoming outdated. In particular the research aimed to discover:

- whether or not innovations in microelectronics and portable test equipment have made an impact into surveyors' practice
- whether surveyors are aware of, and are making the most of, modern equipment
- whether RICS Guidelines are up to date with practice in these respects.

The research was carried out using a postal questionnaire, which was sent together with a stamped addressed envelope and an individually addressed covering letter to 500 building surveyors located throughout the UK. Just under 30% of the questionnaires were returned. The questionnaire was devised following a literature review of all possible items of equipment that could be used during a survey. The items were grouped under the following headings:

- recording/viewing devices
- linear measurement and alignment
- environmental
- material detectors
- electrical testing
- services testing
- metals
- timber
- concrete/mortar
- plastics
- brick/stone
- flat roofs.

The individual items of equipment and the results for each of the four main services investigated (both types of detailed residential survey discussed earlier in this chapter, stock condition surveys and commercial building surveys) are summarised in Table 6.1.

The research revealed no great surprises, and as the results of the commercial building survey are fairly typical these will be discussed here. In the recording/ viewing section 27 surveyors (23%) said that they generally or occasionally used an endoscope. This is quite a high percentage for a fairly specialist item of equipment. As indicated above, the RICS guidance note indicated that optical probes are not normally used. This result from the study suggests that there may be a trend towards their more frequent use.

Table 6.1 Percentages of surveyors using equipment

Equipment	Homebuyer Report (n = 60)	Domestic building survey (n = 113)	Commercial building survey (n = 115)	Stock condition survey (n = 42)
Recording/viewing				
Thermal image camera	0	0	0	2.4
Digital camera	43.3	57.5	63.5	61.9
Video camera	1.7	8.0	18.3	19.0
35 mm camera	45.0	71.7	78.3	64.3
Endoscope	8.3	18.6	23.5	21.4
Hand lens	16.7	17.7	19.1	4.8
Binoculars	86.7	92.9	93.9	73.8
Inspection mirror	41.7	64.6	55.7	31.0
Compass	63.3	62.8	51.3	45.2
Battery torch	91.7	95.6	95.7	76.2
Electric survey lighting	16.7	19.5	17.4	14.3
Dictaphone	60.0	64.6	67.0	47.6
Microscope	0	0	0.9	0
Image analysis software	0	0.9	0.9	0
PC with word processor or spreadsheet	8.3	5.3	8.7	19.0
PC with diagnostic software	0	0	1.7	9.5
Measurement				
Steel tape	53.3	68.1	69.6	57.1
Fabric tape	81.7	76.1	79.1	54.8
Electronic measure	31.7	35.4	47.8	42.9
Tread-wheel	1.7	1.8	5.2	4.8
Crack width measurer	28.3	44.2	44.3	31.0
Movement measurer	20.0	38.1	37.4	26.2
Level	45.0	55.8	49.6	26.2
Plumb-line etc	35.0	46.9	41.7	26.2
Environmental				
Thermometer	15.0	20.4	21.7	19.0
Hygrometer	11.7	17.7	18.3	11.9
Anemometer	0	0	0.9	0
Carbon dioxide detector	0	0.9	0	0
Radon detector	0	0	0	0
Light meter	0	0	3.5	2.4

Table 6.1 Percentages of surveyors using equipment – *continued*

Equipment	Homebuyer Report (*n* = 60)	Domestic building survey (*n* = 113)	Commercial building survey (*n* = 115)	Stock condition survey (*n* = 42)
Noise meter	0	1.8	1.7	0
Moisture meter: pin probe	86.7	86.7	87.0	64.3
Moisture meter: surface	41.7	37.2	40.0	33.3
Moisture meter: other	6.7	6.2	6.1	2.4
Material detectors				
'Studmaster'	5.0	10.6	7.8	11.9
Metal detector	16.7	16.8	14.8	9.5
Electrical testing				
Earth meter	11.7	11.5	10.4	4.8
Mains tester	5.0	14.2	13.9	11.9
Other tester	8.3	8.8	4.3	2.4
Drain testing				
CCTV	1.7	1.8	0.9	0
Smoke bomb	5.0	6.2	1.7	2.4
Fluid dye	6.7	8.8	7.0	4.8
Bung/balloon stopper	11.7	12.4	8.7	0
Metals				
Electronic paint gauge	0	0	0	0
Timber				
Integrity awl	20.0	22.1	19.1	19.0
'Sibert' integrity drill	0	0	0	0
Concrete/mortar				
Chemical analysis kit	0	0	0.9	0
ISAT permeability	0	0	1.7	0
Rebound hammer	0	0	3.5	0
Reinf. cover meter	0	0	0	0
Radar survey	0	0	0	0
Ultrasonic pulse velcty. kit	0	0	0	0
Plastics 'Durometer'	0	0	0	0

Table 6.1 Percentages of surveyors using equipment – *continued*

Equipment	Homebuyer Report (*n* = 60)	Domestic building survey (*n* = 113)	Commercial building survey (*n* = 115)	Stock condition survey (*n* = 42)
Brick/stone				
Ultrasonic pulse velcty. kit	0	0	0	0
Flat roofs				
Leak detector	1.7	0.9	1.7	0

Seventy-three (63%) made use of a digital camera and 77% used a dictaphone. As will be seen from the 'linear measurement' section, a wide range of other measurement aids (apart from a simple tape measure) are used, including an electronic measure (48%). A steel or fabric tape will of course be used to carry out measured surveys as well as to undertake the measurement necessary in connection with a survey of condition. Many surveyors still prefer to use a folding timber rod for carrying out measured surveys.

In the environmental section 22% used a thermometer, and 18% used a hygrometer. As is to be expected, moisture meters of various types were the most used aid in this section. It has long been a requirement that a moisture meter be used during any assessment of condition. Limited use is made of metal detectors: 22 surveyors (19%) used some form of detector. A total of 28 (24%) of the sample used an item of electrical testing equipment. Certainly in the field of domestic inspections there is an increasing trend for the surveyor to carry out some form of rudimentary electrical test (in the United States it is common for the home inspector to test mechanical and electrical services). However, many commentators believe that any test of the electrical installation can be carried out only by a qualified electrician, and that plug testers '...are probably more misleading than helpful'.[5] These results may however indicate the beginning of a trend for surveyors to take greater responsibility for inspection and testing of the electrical installations of buildings. Smaller numbers of surveyors are prepared to carry out their own drain tests, although apparently there is one surveyor out there who carries out CCTV inspections.

Although 22 surveyors (19%) used an integrity awl for testing timber it was with the results of the materials testing section that the researchers were most disappointed. Very small numbers were using any equipment to test concrete and mortar, and none of the sample used anything to test metals, plastics or brick and stone. Two surveyors used a leak detector for flat roofs.

This research has revealed that new technology has made some impact, in that more surveyors are using digital cameras and electronic measurement aids, but little use is being made of portable materials-testing equipment. This may be (as one respondent indicated on the questionnaire) because in most cases surveys are carried out of other people's buildings, and any procedure that involves even the slightest damage would be resisted by owners. The results have indicated that there are increasing trends in the use of endoscopes, some environmental measuring aids, metal detectors and electrical installation testing by surveyors. A follow-up survey is planned to see whether the trends identified by this survey continue, in which case there may be an argument for updating the advice given to surveyors in the guidance notes. The results of the analysis of this study data suggest that most surveyors prefer to rely on what they have relied on for centuries: their senses and in particular their eyesight.

6.4   Summary

The various published guidance is very specific about the equipment that the surveyor should use when inspecting dwellings, but there is less information available for those surveying commercial buildings. An investigation of current practice has indicated that very few surveyors carry out any form of materials testing, but that there may be a trend towards the increased use of endoscopes, environmental testing, metal detection and electrical testing.

Notes

1 RICS *A Guidance Note for Surveyors: Building Surveys of Residential Property* (The Royal Institution of Chartered Surveyors, London, 1996).
2 SAVA *Benchmark Standards for the Homebuyer Survey and Valuation* (Surveyors and Valuers Accreditation, Woking, 2000).
3 RICS *A Guidance Note for Surveyors: Building Surveys and Inspections of Commercial and Industrial Property* (The Royal Institution of Chartered Surveyors, London, 1998).
4 A. Coday and M. Hoxley 'The portable test equipment being used for commercial building surveys' *Structural Survey*, Vol. 19 (2001), No. 3, pp 173–184.
5 P. Parnham and C. Rispin *Residential Property Appraisal* (Spon Press, London, 2001).

7 Planning the survey

7.1 Arriving on site

The surveyor has taken instructions in writing, has organised specialists to assist, has carried out preliminary research, and has arrived on site with the appropriate equipment. The surveyor is now ready to undertake the most important and demanding of the activities involved with a survey – the actual inspection. During the early stages of an inspection it is essential to clear the mind so that the task in hand can be carried out with the full level of skill demanded by the client. The surveyor will probably have arrived on site thinking about the previous job, and it is essential to forget about this and focus upon the property to be inspected. This is easier with an empty property than with one that is occupied. If the existing owner or occupier is present during the inspection there is always the danger that the surveyor could be distracted by their presence. It is important for the surveyor to be single-minded in carrying out the inspection and to 'lose' the occupier as soon as possible after arriving on site.

The other essential element of the preliminary part of a survey is to quickly become familiar with the property – with the extent of the buildings and site. A good method of achieving all of these objectives (the 3 Fs – focus, familiarity and freedom) is to carry out a measured survey of the plot and building's footprint and on the plan to plot a sketch roof plan. This is all essential information that needs to be recorded during the inspection, and by the time this fairly mechanistic and straightforward task has been completed the occupier will usually have lost interest and returned to the interior of the building, while the surveyor will now be aware of the extent of the site and buildings, and should be concentrating fully on the survey.

7.2 Sequence of inspection

Authorities differ on the question of whether it is better to commence the full inspection internally or externally. Many suggest that it is better to inspect internally first, as this will cause the least inconvenience to the occupier,[1] but others seem to suggest that commencing with an external inspection follows more logically the order in which it is usual to report.[2] The author favours the latter approach as he is not particularly concerned with the sensibilities of the occupier, and if anything is missed during the initial inspection of the exterior it is an easy task to re-inspect part of the exterior. It may not be as easy to re-inspect the interior if any problem is suggested by the external inspection.

Say, for example, the inspection of the roof space reveals rain penetration around a chimney stack. If no defect had been identified during the initial external inspection of the stack, it is an easy matter to re-inspect the chimney stack flashings for any sign of a problem. However, let us now assume that the inspection had been carried out in the reverse order and that no defect had been noticed in the roof space. If then a problem with the flashing is identified by the external inspection it may be more difficult to gain access to the roof space for the second time (perhaps involving unscrewing a trap door, placing dust sheets and erecting a ladder).

In many respects the order of inspection is a matter of the personal preference of the surveyor, but it is most important that the inspection be carried out in a logical sequence with which the surveyor is familiar and that the surveyor is not afraid to retrace his or her steps in order to follow a trail of evidence.

To summarise, the author's preferred sequence for the inspection of the property is as follows:

1. measured survey of the plot and footprint of the building
2. inspection of the exterior
3. inspection of the interior.

The exterior inspection will now be considered.

7.3   Inspecting the exterior

It is best to inspect each element of construction in turn as this mirrors the way the report will be structured. However, this is not always practical, particularly where the property being inspected is in the centre of a terrace. In such a situation it is necessary to inspect each elevation in turn, and indeed this is the method of recording information followed by many surveyors, even when inspecting detached or semi-detached structures. Again such choices are largely a matter of personal preference, but whichever method is adopted it is usually best to follow the principle of starting at the top and working down. Thus the following sequence of inspection is recommended:

1 chimney stacks, flashings, cement fillets
2 roofs, pitched and flat main slopes, abutments, ridges, hips, verges, ventilation
3 rainwater goods, gutters, downpipes, gulley or shoe
4 external walls, pointing, movement joints, damp-proof course, subfloor ventilation
5 external joinery, fascias, soffits, windows, doors

6 drainage, foul, above ground, below ground, surface water

7 site, boundaries.

What to actually record during the inspection is discussed further below (section 7.5) and considered in greater detail in the following three chapters. If the building being surveyed is large, the inspection of the exterior will probably have taken at least 1 or 2 hours. Once this is complete it is time to retreat to the interior, where the higher temperature and a welcoming cup of coffee will be much appreciated, particularly during the winter months.

7.4 Inspecting the interior

The dangers of believing any information volunteered by the vendor have been highlighted in Chapter 5, but there will no doubt be some matters that the surveyor wishes to clarify over a reviving beverage (of course the interior of an unoccupied and unheated building can be colder than the exterior, and in such situations the surveyor will have come prepared with a vacuum flask). However, once the essential information has been requested of the occupier it is time to gain one's freedom once again, and a useful ploy to achieve this is to commence the inspection of the interior in the roof space. Few vendors will follow the surveyor into the furthest corners of the roof space, although unfortunately there will always be one or two, including in the author's experience a very sprightly spinster in her seventies who would not let the surveyor out of her sight.

There are however other, perhaps more convincing, reasons for starting in the roof space. First, it continues the logical sequence of starting at the top and working down. Second, it is possible to discover more about the quality of construction in the roof space, where the builder would have made no attempt to disguise any shortcomings, than anywhere else in a building. Third, it is often possible to date a building more precisely from within the roof space. Even if the builder erected no plaque on the elevations to date the building, his tradesmen often left evidence in the form of an engraving in a roof timber or cement rendering to a chimney-breast (or even on some rare occasions a discarded newspaper read during their lunch break). Finally, many defects or matters requiring improvement can be identified in the roof space. This is an area of their dwelling into which many owners or occupiers never venture, and they are often not aware of some of the defects revealed by a survey.

The essential matters that need to be investigated during a roof-space inspection are:

- structural integrity of the frame
- evidence of fungal decay and insect infestation to timber members

- condition of the underside of roof coverings or, where felted or boarded, the felt or boarding
- condition of gable and party walls where applicable
- condition of chimney-breasts and flues, including support provided where removed at lower levels
- type and condition of ceilings
- presence of, extent of and condition of insulation
- condition of water tanks and plumbing
- type, age and condition of electrical wiring
- evidence of rodent, bird, bat or wasp infestation
- adequate ventilation.

Once the roof space has been inspected, each room (including circulation areas such as landings and staircases) should be inspected in detail. Again a logical sequence should be followed, such as inspecting in turn:

- ceiling
- each wall (usually four)
- window(s)
- door(s)
- radiator/heater/fireplace
- electrical fittings
- floor.

Again, the philosophy of working downwards from the top has been followed in each room, and the upper floors would probably be inspected before the ground floor (and basement if there is one). The surveyor will already be located at upper floor level after inspecting the roof space, and with any luck the owner or occupier will not be encountered again until the ground floor is reached.

7.5   What should be recorded?

Since the surveyor will need to convert his or her notes into the report it is important that the notes taken reflect what will be required in the report. For each element of construction it is necessary to record the following:

1. design and construction
2. condition
3. cause of any defects (or recommend further investigation)
4. remedial work required.

Here are two examples of the notes recorded during the inspection of elements of a semi-detached house:

Roof

Double pitched with ridge running parallel to road and with hipped end at west side. Slopes covered with plain clay tiles with bonnet hip tiles and half-round ridge tiles.

Slopes even and coverings generally in satisfactory condition. Two tiles to front slope, and one each to side and rear slopes, have slipped and require re-fixing. Ridge and hip tiles well bedded and pointed.

Bedroom 3 (North-east)

Ceiling

Papered finish.

Paper loose at joins and evidence of cracking and bowing in ceiling.

Paper applied over whitewash and old lath and plaster ceiling has lost key.

Take down existing ceiling and replace with plasterboard and Artex.

Obviously each surveyor will develop a personal style of note-taking, and may well abbreviate frequently used terms (if handwriting notes – see section 7.6), but provided each of the four points is considered in the same order for each element inspected, error-free report writing (see Chapter 11) should follow.

7.6   How should the information be recorded?

There are a variety of methods of recording information on site, and each surveyor will develop a preference for the method employed. Each method is considered below:

- Taking notes by long-hand. This is the most time-consuming method, but it should provide a clear record of the inspection to rely upon at a later date, should that be necessary.
- Dictating notes into a portable tape-recorder for transcription back in the office. Provided there are no recording problems this is less time-consuming on site (most people can talk seven times faster than they can write). However, there is the delay while the notes are typed up and before the report can be commenced. There is also the disadvantage of having to dictate out of hearing of the owner or occupier.

- Both of the above methods can be supplemented by the use of site-prepared sketches, and many surveyors prefer to make their notes of each elevation on a sketch of that elevation. This approach has been strongly advocated by one leading authority.[3]
- Notes can be written on a preprinted form or checklist. This method saves time in that the surveyor does not need to write most of the headings, but it can be cumbersome. However, the checklist approach is probably the best method for inexperienced surveyors.
- Dictating the report directly on site, either for word-processing by a secretary or for use directly into speech recognition software – many practices have adopted the latter approach recently. This is the quickest method, and is adopted by many experienced surveyors who do not like to return to the office until after the report is substantially dictated. However, in the case of *Watts v Morrow* (1991)[4] the judge considered that this method did not provide the surveyor with the opportunity for reflective thought, which is most important when considering the property as a whole. The absence of any site notes leads the surveyor open to a claim of negligence when adopting this method. The author suspects that those adopting this approach feel that commercial pressures outweigh the risks of being sued for negligence. No doubt a judge would look more favourably upon a surveyor adopting this approach if there were some sketches with at least a minimum of annotation to record the inspection.
- Entering data directly into a hand-held computer. This method is suitable only for stock condition surveys and not when any large volumes of text need to be included.

7.7 Summary

Once the surveyor has familiarised him or herself with the layout of the building and site, the inspection should commence with the exterior, followed by the interior, and in general a top-down approach should be adopted. Note-taking for each element should record design and construction, condition, cause of defects and then finally any remedial work required. Whichever method of note-taking is used, the most important principle to observe is that there should be a comprehensive record of the inspection, to which to refer, if necessary, at a later date.

What to inspect is considered in the following three chapters. Chapter 8 considers the matters that data provided by professional indemnity insurers suggest are the areas where most negligence claims arise. These are prime areas for the surveyor to concentrate upon. Chapter 9 discusses the inspection of services and environmental issues, and in Chapter 10 the remaining items to inspect are covered.

Notes

1 I. Melville, I. Gordon and P. Murrells *Structural Surveys of Dwelling Houses* (Estates Gazette, London, 1992).

2 M. Hollis *Surveying Buildings* (RICS Books, Coventry, 2000).

3 M. Hollis *Property Services. Part 2: The Exterior* (The Chartered Surveyors' Education Channel Video, 1995).

4 *Watts v Morrow* (1991) 4 All ER 937, CA.

8 The inspection: structure and fabric

8.1 Benchmark standards

One of the bodies established to accredit surveyors to carry out the new home condition reports (HCR) is Surveyors and Valuers Accreditation (SAVA). SAVA has produced benchmark standards that define, in much greater detail than has been attempted previously, exactly what the surveyor will inspect as part of a Homebuyer Survey and Valuation or a building survey. Since the HCR will be an adapted version of the Homebuyer report (but without a valuation) the following detailed discussion describing what and how the surveyor should inspect is based upon these benchmark standards and their associated features, which were published by SAVA in October 2000.[1] In each section the text from the SAVA document is indicated in italics with the author's commentary and illustrative examples shown in plain text.

The information given in the SAVA document is far more than mere advice or guidance. In the future this detailed published information will probably be the minimum level of inspection expected by the courts in assessing whether a professional has been negligent. Every surveyor must therefore be aware of these benchmark standards.

8.2 Key defects

The surveyor will inspect the dwelling to establish whether there are key defects.

The defects listed – dampness, building movement, timber defects and roof coverings and structures – are the ones that have the greatest potential for causing the owner of a house the greatest expense. An analysis of negligence claims for this type of work reveals that these are the defects for which professional indemnity insurers most often settle claims.

8.3 Dampness

The surveyor will use an electronic moisture meter to identify any dampness problems within the property. This will include:

- *the base of all ground floor internal and external walls at approximately 1 metre intervals*
- *the reveals and below the cills of all window or door openings*

- *internal surfaces that show the visual effects of dampness (e.g. staining or mould growth)*
- *any accessible timber components that are likely to be damp including floor joists, floor-boarding, timber skirtings and linings*
- *areas adjacent to sanitary fittings and other fittings that could result in dampness*
- *in the roof-space where dampness is likely. Examples include exposed walls, embedded timber components especially around valley gutters, chimneys and parapet walls. Additionally, sample readings to rafters and purlins will be taken.*

As discussed in Chapter 6, it has long been a requirement that a surveyor use a moisture meter when assessing the condition of a building. However, for the first time the surveyor has been told precisely where that moisture meter should be used. The comprehensiveness of these requirements leaves little room for doubt. When checking for dampness in wall finishes it is essential that the surveyor recognises that the meter actually measures electrical resistance, and if there is any material within the wall finish that will conduct electricity (for example aluminium foil) then a high reading will be obtained. Should high readings be obtained in unexpected situations, where there are no visible signs of dampness, then the wall finish will need to be investigated (with the owner's consent).

In recent years there has been much adverse publicity about the diagnosis of rising dampness and the use of chemically injected damp-proof courses. Many such dpcs have probably been installed unnecessarily over the last 30 years or so. Many have been installed in situations where the problem was actually condensation or where there was an existing dpc but it was bridged by soil, pavings or external rendering (or perhaps imitation stone cladding) to the wall. Other problems that can be confused with rising dampness are plumbing leaks and leaking rainwater goods.

Some authorities question even the existence of the phenomenon of rising dampness. Such authorities have stood bricks in tanks of water and have been unable to notice any appreciable rise of water up the bricks. The author does not subscribe to the view that there is no such thing as rising dampness, and has witnessed it in a terrace of houses that were built upon a plinth of Staffordshire blue engineering bricks. The dampness was rising not through the very dense and almost impermeable bricks but through the old lime mortar. The chemical injection of a damp-proof course into such a dense material (flint is another material in which similar problems occur) is thoroughly inappropriate. In such situations the physical insertion of a damp-proof course may be the only option. Where the walling material is more permeable, chemical injection may be appropriate provided that a reputable company can be engaged to carry out such work. Members of the British Wood Preserving and Damp-Proofing Association (BWPDA),[2] who offer an insurance-backed guarantee in the event of failure, are more reputable than many contractors in the industry.

When a damp-proof course has been installed it is also necessary to replace the plaster or other finish that has been affected by dampness (the affected area is rarely more than 1 m high). The damp plaster will contain hygroscopic salts, which may continue to attract dampness from the atmosphere even after the original source of dampness has been removed. When re-plastering it is essential to use a cement and sand render coat, preferably including a salt inhibitor or waterproofing agent. This can then be finished with a skim coat of a gypsum-based plaster. It is surprising how often rising dampness following the installation of a dpc is due to the use of a gypsum-based undercoat (such as Carlite) instead of a cement and sand render coat. Another common problem is to carry the render coat down so that it is in contact with the floor; the rendering should be stopped short of the floor by about 25 mm. The existence of a previously installed chemical dpc is usually evidenced by a row of small-diameter holes in a brick course or courses at low level (see Figure 8.1).

Most penetrating dampness problems are caused by leaking or overflowing rainwater goods, but other causes may be missing vertical damp-proof courses or driving rain passing through poorly pointed solid walls in severely exposed locations (such as on a cliff top). Cavity fill that occupies the entire cavity can lead to penetrating dampness in similarly exposed locations. The advice to be given when dealing with a penetrating dampness problem is first to remove (or provide a barrier to) the source of dampness and second to treat damp-affected plaster in the same way as for rising dampness.

As indicated above, condensation is often confused with rising (and indeed penetrating) dampness, but the diagnosis of condensation is a far from straightforward process. Even if condensation is suspected it is difficult to be precise about the necessary remedial work following a single inspection. This is

Figure 8.1 Evidence of a chemical injected dpc

because choices made by occupants of the property can influence the severity of the problem. Perhaps the most common problem is failure to heat the dwelling adequately. An average temperature of about 15°C is the critical level below which condensation can develop. Many occupants on a low budget often make the situation worse by their choice of space-heating method. Portable heating appliances using bottled gas create large volumes of water vapour, which can increase the risk of condensation occurring. Failure to ventilate adequately so that moist air is removed from the building is another contributing factor. In addition to an overall air change of about one per hour throughout the dwelling, high-risk areas such as bathrooms and kitchens require additional mechanical ventilation. Tumble driers should have ducted ventilation direct to the exterior, and cooking hobs should ideally have similar arrangements. One of the worst examples of roof-space condensation the author has seen was due to an occupier venting a cooker hob through the ceiling of the bungalow directly into the roof space.

Since surface condensation occurs when warm air comes into contact with a cold surface that is below the dew-point temperature, another method of remedying the problem may involve upgrading the thermal insulation of the wall or ceiling upon which condensation is occurring. Mould growth is usually the first indication of condensation and is essentially moisture dependent, as the other two ingredients necessary for growth (a source of infection and a source of nourishment) are always present in buildings. There are many varieties of mould spores, and some can germinate at relative humidities (RH) as low as 80%. The mould will spread if the RH is over 70% for long periods – usually more than 12 hours' duration. Remedial work will include washing the mould-affected area with a fungicidal wash or bleach solution, but this will be effective only in conjunction with a mixture of heating, ventilation and insulation.

8.4   Building movement

The surveyor will carry out careful visual inspection for signs of past or continuing building movement. This will include examining:

- *all external and internal wall surfaces*
- *all floor and ceiling surfaces*
- *all roof surfaces and accessible roof spaces*
- *gullies*
- *external areas, gardens, paths and grounds*

and identifying:

- *the location of trees and drain positions.*

Where movement is noticed or suspected, the surveyor should record the extent of the problem. This may include crack width and other characteristics including amount of misalignment or bulging and effects on serviceability (e.g. sticking windows and doors) so a judgement can be made and appropriate advice given.

The final bullet point of the SAVA benchmark requirement identifies the two main culprits as far as subsidence is concerned: vegetation growth on shrinkable clay soils, and leaking drains on mainly (but not exclusively) non-cohesive soils such as sands and gravels. One cannot begin to assess the causes of subsidence without a knowledge of the subsoil upon which the property is built, and the surveyor should have an intimate knowledge of the geology in the area in which he or she practises, or access to detailed geological maps if carrying out surveys over a wide geographical area.

Some definitions are useful at this point:

- *Settlement* is the natural compaction of the soil due to the load imposed by the building. It occurs soon after construction, and causes damage only if it is differential – due perhaps to variations in ground conditions, old foundations or different foundation depths.
- *Subsidence* is 'the downward movement of a building foundation caused by loss of support of the site beneath the foundations'.[3]
- *Heave* is the upward movement of the soil due to its recovering its water content. This is usually caused by the removal of trees on clay soils, but can also be caused by frost action on sand/gravel soils.

Subsidence, heave and settlement (and also landslip) are all caused by movement of the soil upon which the building is founded, but there are other types of building movement that are caused by some failure of the materials of which the property is constructed. Examples of this second type of failure are thermal movement, moisture movement, sulphate attack, cavity wall tie corrosion and lack of lateral restraint. Movement caused by foundation failure tends to be more serious and more expensive to remedy, so this type of movement will be considered first. Before that, however, the actual detection and assessment of movement will be considered.

8.4.1 Detection and assessment of building movement

Before the Second World War most brickwork mortars contained little cement and were generally of lime and sand. Brickwork built with lime and sand mortar is able to accommodate minor movement without cracking, but the rigid-jointed brickwork of postwar property will usually crack if there is any movement. The

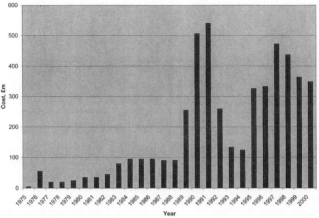

Figure 8.2 Subsidence repair costs
(Data supplied by the Association of British Insurers)

author inspected one house that was built on a raft foundation that suffered from subsidence during the East Coast floods of the 1950s. The raft had tilted, and the entire property had a significant lean, but there was not a single crack to be seen in any external or internal wall. Such cases are unusual, however, and most postwar buildings that have suffered from foundation failure or any other type of movement will exhibit cracking.

To fully understand the current situation in relation to the weight given to cracking when assessing movement of residential buildings it is necessary to view the problem from an insurance industry perspective. Settlement is not, and never has been, covered by domestic insurance policies; subsidence was covered by most policies from about 1971, and heave is covered by some policies.
Following the long hot summers of 1976, 1989 and 1995 there were significant volumes of claims made on insurance policies (see Figure 8.2). Much of the expense of these claims, particularly following the 1976 damage, was for foundation underpinning that many experts believe was unnecessary. In order to provide an objective framework for assessing damage, Building Research Establishment Digest 251 was introduced in 1981 (and amended in 1995).[4] The digest presents six categories of damage ranging from 0 (negligible) to 5 (the most severe where cracks are over 25 mm in width): see Table 8.1. The BRE emphasises that crack width is just one factor in assessing the category of damage, but the information in Table 8.1 is useful as it gives an indication of the likely repair works for the six categories of damage. The cracking shown in Figure 8.3 is clearly Category 5, whereas that sketched in Figure 8.5 is only Category 2.

Despite the objective information provided by BRE Digest 251 much unnecessary underpinning still goes on today. This is due partly to pressure brought by policyholders who are unwilling to accept the BRE's advice that cracks up to say

Table 8.1 Classification of visible damage to walls, with particular reference to ease of repair of plaster and brickwork or masonry*

Damage category	Description of typical damage	Typical size of crack	Ease of repair
0	Hairline cracks classed as negligible	Less than about 0.1 mm	No action required
1	Fine cracks with damage generally restricted to internal wall finishes; cracks rarely visible in external brickwork	Up to 1 mm	Treated easily using normal decoration
2	Cracks not necessarily visible externally; doors and windows may stick slightly	Up to 5 mm	Cracks easily filled; recurrent cracks can be masked by suitable linings; some external pointing may be required to ensure weathertightness; doors and windows may require easing and adjusting
3	Doors and windows sticking; service pipes may fracture; weather tightness often impaired	5–15 mm (or several of say 3 mm)	Cracks require some opening up and can be patched by a mason; repointing of external brickwork and possibly a small amount of brickwork to be replaced
4	Extensive damage, especially over doors and windows; windows and door frames distorted, floor sloping noticeably,† walls leaning or bulging noticeably, † some loss of bearing in beams; service pipes disrupted	15–25mm (but depends on number of cracks)	Requires breaking out and replacing sections of walls
5	Structural damage; beams lose bearing, walls lean badly and require shoring; windows broken with distortion; danger of instability	Greater than 25 mm (but depends on number of cracks)	Requires a major repair job, involving partial or complete rebuilding

*Crack width is one factor in assessing category of damage, and should not be used on its own as a direct measure of it.
†Local deviation of slope, from horizontal or vertical, of more than 1/100 will normally be clearly visible. Overall deviations in excess of 1/150 are undesirable.
Source: Based on Table 1 of BRE Digest 251:1995. Reproduced by permission of BRE.

Figure 8.3 Category 5 masonry cracking to front elevation of a terraced house

5 mm in width are nothing to worry about; but it is also due to the wish for a 'quick fix' – a once and for all repair that does away with the necessity for prolonged monitoring of the movement over several months or even years. Research by one experienced insurance loss adjuster has revealed that in 282 cases of subsidence damage the only factor that was consistently of relevance to the decision to underpin was the actual size of the crack.[5]

When assessing building movement the surveyor must initially categorise the damage in accordance with BRE Digest 251. The precise locations and sizes of cracks should be noted, and in most instances it will be necessary to sketch the affected elevations and any damaged walls and ceilings internally. It takes considerable experience to be able to identify the width of a crack without physically measuring it. The best way to measure cracks is with a crack-width gauge such as that illustrated in Figure 8.4. Sketching serves two purposes. First, it

Figure 8.4 Proprietary crack width gauge

provides a record of the damage at the time of inspection so that if the surveyor is called back many months later it is possible to say whether any further movement has occurred. Second, by preparing sketches such as that shown in Figure 8.5 the surveyor will begin to develop an awareness of how the building is moving.

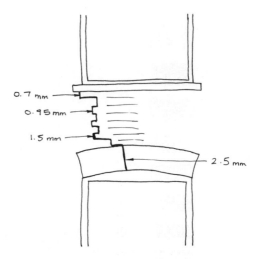

Figure 8.5 Sketch to record masonry cracking

Cracking due to foundation movement usually extends above and below the dpc, affects both internal and external surfaces, is usually diagonal in direction, and is usually tapered (that is, of uneven width). It is in the assessment of tapered cracks that the surveyor should be able to see whether various parts of the building are moving up or down in relation to one another (see Figure 8.6). Obviously the

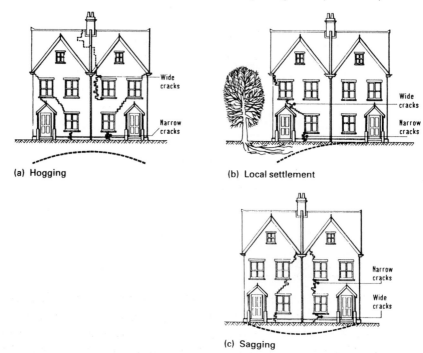

Figure 8.6 Typical foundation movement cracking
(Based on Figure 13 in CIRIA Report 111)

correct diagnosis of the direction of movement is essential since it is necessary to be able to differentiate between subsidence and heave, and to be able to see which parts of the building are affected by the movement.

Once the cracking has been recorded and categorised it is then necessary to determine the likely age of the cracking. This is not as easy as it sounds. In areas of heavy pollution the interior surfaces of a recent crack should be lighter in colour than the face of the wall. If there is dirt, moss or other vegetation evident inside the crack then it is likely to be older. Internally the age of decorations can give a clue as to the age of the crack. If the decorations are old and there is evidence of previous filling of the crack then it is safe to assume that it is old. However, it may still be moving (see below). If the decorations are recent and the crack seems to have developed since redecoration then it is likely to be a recent crack. If surveying for the owner then one may be able to obtain more reliable information than when surveying for a potential purchaser. Some owners are very forthcoming and will say exactly when the crack appeared. The author was called out by one owner to investigate a 25 mm wide crack that had appeared overnight in the internal wall between the main front and rear rooms of the house. The crack seemed to be growing larger every second, and it was fairly easy to discover that it had been caused by a burst water main under the house, which was founded on a sand subsoil. Unfortunately not all building movement problems are this easy to diagnose.

If the surveyor concludes that the movement has been caused by foundation movement and that it appears recent, the next question to be asked is: What is causing the movement? As indicated at the beginning of this section the two main causes are trees and drains, and these are discussed in more detail below. If, however, there are either of these two hazards present in close proximity to the area of damage then it is appropriate to recommend further investigation. Such investigation is likely to involve digging trial holes, testing the watertightness of drain runs and, if trees are suspected, possibly calling in an arboriculturalist. Once the cause of the movement is removed or alleviated it will then be necessary to monitor the building over a period of time before deciding on the necessary remedial works. Clearly such further investigation and monitoring is beyond the scope of the original instructions if these were merely to carry out a survey. The surveyor's professional duty is to record the extent of the movement at the time of the survey, to say whether he or she thinks it is recent, to suggest possible causes, and to recommend appropriate further investigations.

Other causes of foundation failure are landslip — where one expanse of soil moves in relation to another (usually downhill) — and mining subsidence. If a surveyor is practising in an area where mining has taken place in the past then he or she will no doubt be aware of the location of most workings and will have access to a map showing the main mines. Not all workings are indicated on these maps, however, and some small shafts that were worked for only a short period of time by small companies may not be properly recorded.

The two principal causes of foundation failure – leaking drains and trees – will now be considered in more detail.

8.4.2 Drains

Most drains laid before 1970 had rigid socket and spigot joints formed with cement, and such drains are not able to accommodate ground movement. Plastic-sleeved joints of rigid pipes were used from about 1970, and flexible uPVC drains with flexible joints have been used for the last 10–15 years. There was a short period during the 1960s when pitch fibre pipes were common, and many of these pipes have suffered from either blockage or leakage due to their being compressed by the weight of soil above them. The author practised for many years on the coast in Norfolk, where a combination of rigid-jointed drains and non-cohesive soils (originally beach sand) led to many subsidence problems in properties built before 1960.

Where there are trees and shrubs close to drain runs, roots can further damage a slightly leaking drain, and the presence of roots should be checked for in inspection chambers. If there are drains close to the area of damage then the watertightness of the drains should be checked (see section 4.3). If the drains are indeed leaking then it will be necessary to repair or more likely replace them. The cracking should then be monitored (see section 8.4.5 below), and if no further movement occurs then the cracks can be repaired and any other necessary remedial works carried out. It is only when there has been severe leakage that has washed away the soil beneath foundations that further movement may occur necessitating the underpinning of foundations.

Most buildings' insurance policies do not cover damaged pipes, so the drain repairs do not form a legitimate expense under the claim. What is covered by most policies is damage caused by leaking pipes, and therefore the cost of any underpinning and the cosmetic repair work can be recovered. Perhaps this is another reason why much underpinning has been carried out unnecessarily in the past. Note that building control approval is required for drain replacement work.

8.4.3 Trees

The predominant subsoil type in the south-east of England is shrinkable clay, and it was not until after the 1976 drought that the Building Regulations were amended to require a minimum foundation depth of 1.0 m on clay soils. Where there are trees or vegetation close to a proposed building on clay subsoils then foundation depths are required to be very much deeper – that is, below any root growth – and this usually involves the use of trench fill or piled foundations. It is generally accepted that global warming will involve more frequent extremes of weather, and it is possible that more severe droughts than we have experienced before will lead to subsidence problems in many houses built before 1960 that have so far shown no sign of any problem. Similarly, as trees grow and extract more water from clay subsoils in drought conditions it is certain that there will continue to be more subsidence problems due to desiccation of the soil.

Trees are an important part of the urban landscape, and if all trees that could adversely affect buildings were to be removed then this landscape would be ruined in many of our towns and cities. The traditional advice about the proximity of trees to buildings on clay subsoils is that the tree should be at least its mature height away from any buildings, and that where there are groups of trees these should be at least one and a half times their mature height away. Of course not all trees present the same risk. The species that extract most water from the soil include poplar, willow, oak, elm, horse chestnut and sycamore. One authority recommends that the surveyor carry a tree identification handbook at all times.[6] The same writer[7] suggests a method for estimating the height of the tree by marking angles on a piece of paper and sighting the top of the tree along one of these lines from a known distance from the tree. Simple trigonometry can then be used to estimate the height of the tree. Parnham and Rispin report research that suggests that the traditional guidance on the distances from tree to building may be over-cautious. They report[8] that an insurance company has discovered that 90% of damage to property on shrinkable soils occurred when the trees were within the following distances:

- 20 m for high water demand trees
- 10 m for medium water demand trees.

If a mature tree is discovered to be causing subsidence it is not possible merely to remove it as the resultant increase in water volume of the soil would cause heave to occur. A possible solution is for the height of the tree to be reduced gradually, and the surveyor will probably feel obliged to recommend that his client consult an arboriculturalist if such solutions are proposed.

Trees can cause other problems apart from subsidence on clay soils. Their leaves can block gutters, including vulnerable internal valley and parapet gutters, and buildings can be badly damaged by falling trees. Figure 8.7 shows the fire brigade about to remove a tree that had been uprooted by the hurricane of 16 October 1987. The tree was in danger of falling onto the front of the adjacent house until

Figure 8.7 Fire brigade removing tree uprooted by the 1987 hurricane. The left-hand ladder was used to prop the tree to prevent it from falling onto the house

the owner propped it with an aluminium ladder. The owner's insurance company was happy to pay for a new ladder instead of the substantial reconstruction of the bay at the front of the house.

8.4.4 Secondary causes of movement

As mentioned above, less serious but nevertheless substantial movement can occur as a result of problems with the method of construction. Cracking from such defects does not usually extend below the dpc, and it is the pattern that the cracking takes that generally enables these defects to be identified. The main defects are as follows.

Thermal movement of masonry walls
Large expanses of masonry require vertical movement joints to allow for thermal expansion and contraction, and these should be provided at 12 m centres. Defects of this type are particularly prevalent in terraces, where vertical cracks will be seen at the weakest points – generally above and below window openings. Remedial works are difficult, as movement will continue unless a physical expansion joint is installed. The extent of cracking is usually small and does not warrant the expense of forming such a joint.

Moisture movement of masonry
The most common example of this type of movement is the drying shrinkage of calcium silicate (sand-lime) bricks. Unless movement joints are provided when

Figure 8.8 Shrinkage cracking in calcium silicate brickwork

using such bricks then some cracking will usually occur (see Figure 8.8). The cracking generally follows the mortar joints, and these joints can be re-pointed once the cracking has occurred. Since sand – lime bricks have smooth faces and are of a very regular and consistent size and shape, the re-pointed joints always look rather unsightly.

Sulphate attack of clay brickwork

Naturally occurring sulphates in the clay from which the bricks are fired combine with a by-product of the cement in the mortar to produce calcium sulpho-aluminate. The crystals of this material expand, causing expansion of the brickwork, which results in 'map-like' cracking and sometimes bulging, both of which are more pronounced towards the top of the wall, which is generally wetter. Sulphate attack is more of a problem with chimney stacks and parapet walls but can also affect walls. If the problem persists then re-pointing with a sulphate-resisting cement may be necessary. Efflorescence is a much less serious problem; here the white deposits caused by salts being brought to the surface of new clay brickwork by rain will eventually disappear or can be brushed off.

Cavity wall tie corrosion

Research by the BRE suggests that any cavity wall built before the standard for galvanising steel ties was upgraded in 1981 is likely to fail before the expected life of the building is reached. Cavity walls were adopted generally in the UK in the inter-war period but there are earlier examples dating to before the beginning of the twentieth century. Early wall ties were often formed from iron or steel with no protective coating whatsoever. Later examples were protected with a coat of bitumen. Corrosion and expansion of the ferrous metal causes horizontal cracking in the bed joints in which the ties are located. Thus there will horizontal cracks in every sixth course or so. The cracking will be more pronounced on exposed elevations and towards the top of the wall, where the weight of the wall is less. Some of the worst examples of wall tie failure are to be found on exposed coasts where the salt-laden air causes greater corrosion. If re-pointing of occasional horizontal joints is evident during the inspection then wall tie corrosion should be suspected. Occasionally the wall will bulge outwards, and in such instances some rebuilding may be required. It is more usual, however, to remove the corroded ties and to substitute stainless steel ties, often embedded in epoxy resin and then tensioned. A whole industry has developed to carry out this work, and as with any other activity a reputable contractor should be recommended. The appropriate further investigation work to recommend if wall tie failure is suspected is for a borescope inspection to be carried out by a reputable specialist contractor.

Lack of lateral restraint
It is slightly more than 25 years since the Building Regulations were amended to require lateral restraint to be provided to external walls at floor and roof level. Where in particular the floor joists run parallel to a flank wall of a building built before the mid-1980s then some form of bulging may be expected. The problem is often accentuated by the presence of the stairs adjacent to this wall. The extent of bulging should be measured with the aid of a plumb line. CIRIA offers the following advice as to the stability of bulging walls:[9]

- Where the wall is not well restrained, it retains a precarious equilibrium with leans or bulges of up to 85% of wall thickness (assuming a solid wall) provided it supports no loading from an upper storey or beam.
- With adequate restraint, the wall will support a concentric load while still retaining a precarious equilibrium at leans or bulges of up to 85% of wall thickness.

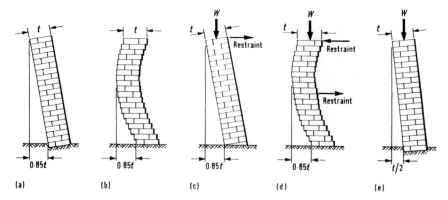

Figure 8.9 Stability of free-standing and restrained walls
(Based on Figure 12 in CIRIA Report 111)

- An unrestrained wall supporting a concentric load reaches precarious equilibrium at 50% of wall thickness.

See Figure 8.9 for an illustration of these principles. This advice provided comfort for many investigators, and also inspires ideas for strengthening walls that are poorly restrained.[10]

Roof spread

This is another relatively common problem, which can cause bulging and cracking of masonry walls. Sometimes the spread is caused by re-roofing with a heavier covering than existed previously without strengthening the roof structure, and sometimes by alteration or deterioration of the roof structure. It is common to see relatively minor cracking at high level to walls to which the roof is not tied down. This is caused by slight uplift of the roof during very heavy wind loading, and in most instances is not serious enough to warrant remedial work. The worst example of roof spread that the author has witnessed was the result of the tenant of a bungalow deciding to remove some rather important trussed rafter members in order to enlarge the room available for a model railway in the roof space!

Figure 8.10 Studs monitoring movement of crack in party wall of terraced house. The crack is in the roof space, and the chimney-breasts have been temporarily shored
(Photo courtesy of the Fordham Johns Partnership)

8.4.5 Monitoring movement

Reference has been made earlier in this chapter to the need to monitor building movement over time. In addition to the careful measurement of cracks it is necessary to measure the extent of movement on either side of the cracks. This is best done by fixing studs with epoxy resin into the masonry on either side of the cracks, as illustrated in Figure 8.10. By taking precise measurements between the centres of the studs or screws at regular intervals of time the extent of any movement can be assessed. An alternative is to use proprietary calibrated tell-tales, but in the author's experience these are not always clear to read and are more easily affected by the weather and sometimes by vandals. The least effective method is to use glass tell-tales, which will only tell you one thing if they break – that the building has moved!

8.5   Timber defects

The surveyor will carry out a careful visual inspection of a reasonable proportion of accessible timber surfaces for evidence of any past and/or continuing rot or woodworm. This will also include external and internal painted joinery items. The timber components will be tested with an electronic moisture meter as described in the section on dampness mentioned above.

Timber defects may be classified as those caused by insect infestation and those caused by fungal attack. The advice for the treatment of timber defects has changed significantly within recent years in response to concerns about the extent of damage caused by the removal of sound timber and environmental concerns about the amounts of chemicals that have been used in the past. These chemicals have been shown to have been harmful to animals that live in and around buildings and also to their human occupants. Some of the most up-to-date advice on the detection and remediation of timber defects is to be found in a BRE document.[11] A brief summary of the essential matters a surveyor requires to know follows.

8.5.1 Wood-boring insects

A number of insects (mainly beetles) are able to use wood as a food source, and some can cause serious damage to building timbers. The typical life cycle is larva (worm) for 1–5 years, pupa (larva to adult) for 6 weeks, and adult (beetle) for 2–3 weeks. The adult mates, and lays eggs on the surface of, or in crevices of, wood to start the cycle off again. Insects may be classified into those for which insecticidal treatment is usually needed and those for which treatment is necessary only to control the associated wood rot. In the latter case the insects (such as bees, wasps, weevils and wharf borer, tenebrionid and stag beetles) attack only rotten timber. Insects for which insecticidal treatment is necessary are considered below.

Common furniture beetle (Anobium punctatum)
This is the most common type of infestation, and is commonly known by the name woodworm. It can attack softwood and European hardwoods, but only the sapwood of sound timber. It is frequently found in older furniture, in roof voids, in staircases and in floor timbers that are slightly damp. The flight holes are circular, 1–2 mm in diameter, and the bore dust (frass) consists of cream-coloured, lemon-shaped pellets, gritty when rubbed between the fingers.

Remedial treatment usually involves organic solvent, emulsion or paste.

Lyctus powderpost beetle (Lyctus brunneus)
This attacks the sapwood of tropical and European hardwoods, principally oak and elm. It is not found in softwoods. It is commonly found in furniture and occasionally in block or strip flooring. The flight holes are circular, 1–2 mm in diameter, and tunnels close to the surface are a feature of attack. The bore dust is cream-coloured, fine and talc-like.

Remedial treatment involves organic solvent or paste.

House longhorn beetle (Hylotrupes bajulus)
This attacks the sapwood of most timbers (particularly roofing timbers). At present it is common only in Surrey, where special building regulations exist; it is rare in other parts of the country. The author is aware of one infestation in a Norfolk seaside town, but here the beetles had been introduced into the property as a result of the occupiers' moving (with their furniture) from Surrey.

The flight holes are large, oval, often ragged, and 6–10 mm across. Extensive infestations have been discovered by hearing larva feeding. The bore dust consists of cream-coloured, sausage-shaped pellets.

Remedial treatment involves organic solvent or paste. Structural timbers often require replacement, and the BRE is to be notified of every attack.

Deathwatch beetle (Xestobium rufovillosum)
This attacks the sapwood and heartwood of partially decayed hardwood, chiefly oak. It is often found in historic buildings, and dampness is essential for establishment and promoting rapid development.

The flight holes are circular, 2–3 mm in diameter, with extensive tunnelling. The bore dust consists of cream-coloured, disc-shaped pellets, gritty when rubbed between the fingers.

Remedial treatment involves organic solvent or paste (sometimes smokes). Remedial measures are necessary to reduce dampness, and a recent EU-funded study by English Heritage[12] has suggested that preservative treatments are ineffective, and that it is more important to solve the dampness problems. New timbers may be placed alongside the affected timbers.

Ptilinus beetle (Ptilinus pectinicornis)
This affects a limited range of European hardwoods – mainly beech, elm, hornbeam and maple. It is found mainly in furniture.

The flight holes are circular, 1–2 mm in diameter. The bore dust is cream-coloured, very densely packed in tunnels and not easily dislodged, but fine and talc-like when crushed and rubbed between fingers.

Treatment may be with organic solvent, emulsion or paste.

Subterranean termites
These have recently been discovered in the south-west of England. Global warming is thought to be a contributory factor. Termites rapidly eat timber-framed structures, and the Government is carrying out an urgent eradication programme.

8.5.2 Wood-rotting fungi

These feed off timber with moisture content above 20%, and therefore occur internally in buildings only if there is a dampness problem: common causes are rising or penetrating dampness, leaking rainwater goods and plumbing.

The main types are:

- *white rots* – cause the wood to become lighter in colour and fibrous in texture without cross-cracking.
- *brown rots* – cause the wood to become darker in colour, and to crack along and across the grain. When dry, very decayed wood will crumble to dust.

Except for one brown rot, *Serpula lacrymans*, which is commonly known as dry rot, all white rots and brown rots are referred to as wet rots.

Wet rots
These can affect softwoods and hardwoods. They are relatively rare internally but common on external joinery. Although there are several types of both white and brown rot, identification is sometimes difficult, and in any event is not crucial since the remedial measures are the same for all wet rots:

- Establish the size and significance of the attack. In particular, if structural timbers are affected a detailed investigation should be carried out to ascertain whether structural repairs are necessary, and if they are, steps should be taken to secure structural integrity.
- Locate and eliminate sources of moisture.
- Promote rapid drying of the structure.
- Remove rotted wood, and apply localised preservative treatment only to timbers that are likely to remain damp for long periods.
- In replacement work, use preservative-treated timbers.
- Introduce support measures, such as ventilation pathways between sound timber and wet brickwork or, where ventilation is not possible, the provision of a barrier such as a damp-proof membrane or joist-hangers between timber and wet brickwork.

Dry rot

This affects mostly softwood, and often causes extensive damage. Remedial works can be very expensive. Dry rot is sensitive to high temperatures (over 25°C) and drying, and is therefore rarely found on exposed timbers or in situations where fluctuating conditions are likely (such as well-ventilated subfloors or roof spaces). It is able to grow through bricks and mortar but requires timber to feed on. Strands can transport moisture from damp areas, allowing the spread of fungus to dry wood in unventilated conditions. Appearance of the fruiting body may be the first indication of an outbreak. Decayed wood has a dull brown colour, typically with deep cracks along and across the grain. It is light in weight, and crumbles between

Figure 8.11 Extensive dry rot attack
(Photograph courtesy of McBain's Cooper)

the fingers. There is no skin of sound wood. The fungal characteristics are silk-white sheets or cotton wool-like mycelium, white to grey strands (sometimes as thick as a pencil), yellow or red fruiting body with white or grey edges, and profuse reddish-brown dust spores (see Figure 8.11).

The remedial treatment for dry rot is as follows:

- Establish the size and significance of the attack. In particular, if structural timbers are affected a detailed investigation should be carried out to ascertain whether structural repairs are necessary and, if they are, steps should be taken to secure structural integrity.
- Locate and eliminate sources of moisture.
- Promote rapid drying of the structure.
- Remove rotted wood, cutting away timber approximately 300–450 mm from the last evidence of fungus or rot.
- Contain the fungus within the wall using preservatives in cases where drying will be delayed.
- In replacement work, use preservative-treated timbers.
- Treat remaining sound timbers that are at risk with preservative (minimum two full brush coats).
- Introduce support measures, such as ventilation pathways between sound timber and wet brickwork or, where ventilation is not possible, the provision of a barrier such as a damp-proof membrane or joist-hangers between timber and wet brickwork.
- Do not retain timber that has been infected by dry rot without seeking expert advice. There is always a risk in retaining infected wood, which can be minimised by preservative treatment and subsequent inspection.[11]

As discussed in Chapter 4, it is one of the core skills of the surveyor to be able to detect both insect infestation and fungal attack of timber, but once it has been detected the advice should always be that a specialist timber treatment company able to offer an insurance-backed guarantee be engaged to carry out the remedial work. Since dry rot remedial works are usually very expensive, the advice of such a specialist should be obtained before entering into a contract to purchase a property affected by dry rot.

In assessing the condition of painted softwood external joinery it is important to use a penknife or other probe to check for wet rot attack and the presence of filler. It is possible for the surface of for example a window sill to appear perfectly satisfactory, but for there to be extensive rot or filler beneath the surface. When reporting upon wet rot attack to external joinery it is often better not to be too specific about where attack has been detected. If for instance rot is discovered in three out of eight windows in a house the client will no doubt express some disquiet if they discover rot in a fourth window. It would be better to report something such as 'extensive wet rot is evident and has affected several windows including those of the dining room, study and bathroom'.

8.6   Roof coverings and structures

The surveyor will carry out a careful visual inspection of all accessible and visible roof coverings and structures, such as chimney stacks and pots, for any evidence of past or continuing defects. Upper roofs will be inspected from the ground through binoculars. Inspection from neighbouring properties and adjacent public areas may be appropriate.

Roofs below 3.0 m above the ground level will either be inspected from an adjacent window and/or from the top of a surveyor's ladder.

The surveyor will inspect all accessible roof voids so that the construction and condition can be assessed.

In this context the word 'structures' is thought to refer to any structure above roof level. In addition to chimney stacks it could include parapet walls, roof-lights, dormer windows, structures to house observation towers and so on. The requirement to use binoculars can lead to slight problems. The author was once questioned by an officer of Her Majesty's Constabulary following a complaint from a neighbour of the property being inspected. The lady in question thought that she was being spied upon!

It is important to inspect both the upper and under surfaces of a roof covering before advising upon any repair or replacement works. The absence of sarking felt or presence of lamination of the underside of roof slates or tiles may have a bearing on the eventual advice given to the client. It is wise to see what has happened to similar neighbouring houses. If most properties in the street have been re-roofed then it fairly safe to assume that the building being inspected will also require re-roofing in the near future.

It is important that, in addition to considering the overall condition of the roof covering and its expected life, the details of the coverings are reported upon. Ridge, verge, hip, valley and abutment details should all be considered. Ventilation (or in older roofs the probable lack of it) should be considered and appropriate advice offered. A roof that is in otherwise satisfactory condition may require re-bedding of ridge tiles or replacement of abutment lead flashings, which have been provided in sections that are too large and which have suffered from thermal movement.

Flat roofs should be treated with great caution. The expected life of a timber-framed flat roof with an old BS 747 felt covering is at the most 10 years. Better-quality, high-performance roofing felts have been used for some years now, but even these have a maximum life of 15–20 years from new. The presence of ventilation is most important with a cold roof deck, and the lack of ventilation of a roof known to have a cold deck should lead the surveyor to report that the roof structure and deck may well be in poor condition. An assessment of the condition of the covering, the effectiveness of any solar reflective finish, the presence of ventilation and the condition of abutment details should lead the surveyor to give an indication of the likely life of the flat roof. Experience suggests that it is always better to be pessimistic in this assessment.

Chimney stack defects to check for include: leaning stacks (which may require rebuilding); sulphate attack, which can often contribute to the stack leaning; poorly pointed brickwork; defective or missing lead flashings (cement mortar fillets may have been provided in inferior construction); and precariously balanced pots and flaunching. Binoculars are particularly useful for inspecting stacks. Where a gas appliance is installed, a stainless steel flue terminal is evidence that the brick flue may have been lined.

The importance of the roof-space inspection was emphasised in Chapter 7. The essential matters that need to be investigated during a roof-space inspection are discussed in greater detail below:

- *Structural integrity of the frame.* This is undoubtedly the most important. Timber member sizes and approximate spans should be recorded so that they can be checked back in the office. Any evidence of excessive deflection or poorly formed joints should be noted. The joints between rafter feet and ceiling joists are particularly important to ensure that no spreading of the roof is occurring. Where there are trussed rafters the wind bracing and lateral restraint arrangements should be checked. The earliest trussed rafters had neither.
- *Evidence of fungal decay and insect infestation to timber members.* These items have been discussed above. If evidence of woodworm is discovered then signs of recent attack (fresh frass or bore dust) should be investigated. It should be borne in mind, however, that there may be such evidence even if the infestation has recently been treated. This is because the beetles may still emerge one last time before being killed by the preservative treatment.
- *Condition of the underside of roof coverings, or where felted or boarded, the felt or boarding.* Tears or gaps in felt should be checked for. When inspecting during snow do not be surprised to discover some of this in the roof space, since snow can be blown through small gaps through which rain will not penetrate.
- *Condition of gable and party walls where applicable.* The author has discovered

evidence of cavity wall tie corrosion on a gable wall that was not readily detectable from an external inspection from ground level.

- *Condition of chimney breasts and flues, including support provided where removed at lower levels.* It is surprising how many chimney breasts are inadequately supported in roof spaces. Support off slender ceiling joists is quite common. Remedial works to recommend will usually involve support by a steel beam. The flues should be checked to ensure that they do not communicate with the roof space. If they do then lining of the flues should be recommended.
- *Type and condition of ceilings.* Where lath and plaster (or even reed and plaster) ceilings exist the limited life of these should be reported on.
- *Presence of, extent of and condition of insulation.* In excess of 200 mm thickness of insulation will soon be the norm for new houses. The eaves should be checked to ensure that insulation does not block ventilation gaps.
- *Condition of water tanks and plumbing.* See Chapter 9.
- *Type, age and condition of electrical wiring.* See Chapter 9.
- *Evidence of rodent, bird, bat and wasp infestation.* See Chapter 10.
- *Adequate ventilation.* If the roof space is well insulated then ventilation should be recommended if it is not present.

Sometimes the inspection of the roof space is hampered because there is an attic room formed within it. The surveyor should check details of the floor joists, staircase access and natural lighting to ensure that the room has been provided in accordance with Building Regulations. Where it is obvious that the loft conversion is a DIY project, this fact should be reported to the client together with the advice that the room is only suitable for light storage purposes. As far as possible the surveyor should check to ensure that the DIY efforts have not weakened the structure of the original roof. Where only opening-up works would confirm this fact then such works should be recommended.

8.7   Summary

This chapter has concentrated on those essential matters that, if discovered during the survey, are likely to involve considerable expense for one's client. These are dampness, building movement, and timber and roof defects. Chapter 9 concentrates on the inspection of the services and consideration of environmental issues.

Notes

1 *Benchmark Standards for the Homebuyer Survey and Valuation* (Surveyors and Valuers Accreditation, Woking, 2000).

2 British Wood Preserving and Damp-Proofing Association, 1 Gleneagles House, Vernon Gate, Derby DE1 1UP. Tel: 01332 225100.

3 *Subsidence of Low Rise Buildings* (The Institution of Structural Engineers, London, 1994).

4 *Assessment of Damage in Low-rise Buildings*, BRE Digest 251 (Building Research Establishment, Watford, 1990).

5 D. Wilkin and R. Baggott 'Technical factors influencing decisions to select underpinning on shrinkable clay' *Structural Survey*, Vol. 12 (1994), No. 2, pp 10–14.

6 M. Hollis *Property Services. Part 2: The Exterior* (The Chartered Surveyors' Education Channel Video, 1995).

7 M. Hollis *Surveying Buildings*, p 506 (RICS Books, Coventry, 2000).

8 P. Parnham and C. Rispin *Residential Property Appraisal*, p 78 (Spon Press, London, 2001).

9 *Structural Renovation of Traditional Buildings*, CIRIA Report 111 (Construction Industry Research and Information Association, London, 1986; reprinted 1994 with update amendments).

10 P. Robson *Structural Repair of Traditional Buildings*, p 200 (Donhead Press, Donhead St Mary, Dorset, 1999).

11 A. Bravery, R. Berry, J. Carey and D. Cooper *Recognising Wood Rot and Insect Damage in Buildings* (Building Research Establishment, Watford, 1997).

12 C. Wood 'Death-watch beetle and its treatment' *Structural Survey* Vol. 17 (1999), No. 3, pp 131–137.

9 The inspection: services and environmental issues

9.1 Benchmark standards

The SAVA benchmarking details[1] for services are, as before, indicated in italics with commentary and illustrative detail provided in plain text.

The surveyor is to carry out a visual examination, that is without test, of the services that are readily available for examination without risk of causing damage to the property or injury to the surveyor.

The surveyor will assess the general condition of the services, identify any obvious non-compliance with safety or other regulations and advise the customer on the need for further tests and examinations by appropriate specialists.

The type of services inspected will normally include:

- *electricity installation*
- *gas installation*
- *plumbing installation*
- *heating and associated system*
- *drainage system*
- *other services.*

The surveyor is to collect enough information so that an opinion can be expressed in relation to:

- *any apparent and urgent health and safety issues*
- *any significant defects that are readily apparent from the visual inspection*
- *the advisability of further tests.*

Surveyors will inspect the service elements in voids and ducts that are inspected during the course of a survey and may include:

- *roof and loft space*
- *beneath any exposed suspended floors and basements*
- *in any tank rooms, cupboards or service ducts.*

Many surveyors do not consider that the services of the building are their responsibility, and carry out only the most casual of inspections. This approach has been challenged recently, and it has been suggested that surveyors need to be far more proactive and practical in their advice about services.[2] British Gas is reportedly training its service engineers to carry out the new home condition reports. They presumably believe that this direct competition to built environment professionals can be justified because the services are such an important part of a dwelling that it will be easy for them to train their engineers to look at the other matters as well. It is likely that this competition will mean that surveyors will have to take on far more responsibility for services in the future. This certainly mirrors the situation of US home inspectors (it is interesting that the Government is proposing that the surveyors' accreditation body will be known as the Home Inspectors Certification Board). For the time being, however, surveyors are to inspect but not test the services.

9.2 Electrical installations

Identify the type, age and general condition of the visible cabling in all accessible locations.

Locate and inspect the meters and associated switchgear.

Identify and inspect a sample of the switches, sockets, fittings and fixed appliances to allow a general assessment of condition and suitability without any form of test.

Identify any obvious hazards or safety issues associated with the electrical installation.

One of the Cambridge colleges proudly proclaims in its prospectus that its dining room has never had an electricity supply connected and that students may dine by candlelight every evening during term. This building must be in a minority of very few in the twenty-first century, but when the author started surveying buildings less than 30 years ago it was not uncommon to discover a house that was still lit by gas and which had no electricity supply connected. It is only just over 100 years since the first electricity supply was made available, and in 1914 most houses did not have a supply. It was only during the 1920s and 1930s that there was a large-scale move from gas lighting to electricity – which could also power appliances.

Electricity is one of the subjects that many surveyors have difficulty in understanding; perhaps it is the abstract nature of electricity that they cannot see, or perhaps they have been turned off by school physics experiments! A brief summary of the essential points that the surveyor needs to know is presented here.

The Institution of Electrical Engineers (IEE) has produced Wiring Regulations that are now industry standard. The Regulations are concerned with the design, installation and testing of electrical circuits. Although not statutory they do constitute good practice, and most electricity companies will supply electricity only to houses wired to the standard set out in the Regulations.

The IEE Regulations cover polarity, earthing, insulation resistance and circuit continuity.

In the past some houses had overhead electrical supplies but the vast majority now have underground supplies. The meter and consumer unit (which contains the fuses) were traditionally placed inside the house. Today the incoming supply cable usually terminates in a cabinet placed on the outside of the house (so that the electricity company can read the meter(s) externally and if necessary disconnect the supply), while the consumer unit remains in the house. The cabinet contains a sealed fuse designed to blow if the fuses in the consumer unit fail to operate. The consumer unit contains the mains switch, which isolates all the circuits in the house. Each circuit will have its own fuse or circuit breaker.

The power circuits of a property built before the Second World War were generally on a *radial system*: individual cables were fed from the fuse box to one or more socket outlets. The circuits were wired and fused for differing purposes: for example, one for small electrical equipment and another for larger equipment. Modern installations have a *ring main system* whereby the cable containing the live, neutral and earth wires runs from the fuse in the consumer unit to serve each socket or appliance in turn, returning in a ring to the consumer unit. There is usually one ring for each floor. As the power flows both ways round the ring the load on the cable is reduced, which permits smaller cable sizes. The total load for a ring main is usually 30 amps. It is unlikely that all sockets will be used at any one time, but if this 30 amp load is exceeded the fuse in the consumer unit will blow. Separate from the ring main there are usually radial circuits running from the consumer unit to supply appliances that are permanently connected and which have a high load (and therefore require a larger cable), such as cooker, immersion heater and shower. The floor area served by a ring main should not exceed 100 m². A radial supply can also be taken off a ring main: this is known as a *spur*, which can serve only one double socket outlet or one fixed appliance (served by a fused connection box).

Older properties had lighting circuits that were arranged in a *junction box system* with a cable run from the fuse box to a series of junction boxes. Each junction box served a light and its switch. In modern houses the lighting is also kept separate from the power circuit. There are usually two circuits – one for each floor – and the wiring is taken to the lights in what is known as a *loop-in system*. The cable runs from the consumer unit to each lighting rose, and a cable of the same size then connects the rose to the switch. Lights do not consume as much power, and the cable does not return to the consumer unit. The circuit is therefore a radial system and is usually protected by a 5 amp fuse, which will carry a load of about 12 100-watt bulbs.

The function of a fuse is to prevent fire or heat damage to cables that are overloaded with electric current. Fuses are located in the consumer unit, with one for each circuit in the house. Fuses are also located in some socket outlets, as well as in the plug of every movable appliance. They are designed to fail before any serious damage occurs to the circuit, and have a current rating less than the cable or appliance they are intended to protect. If too great a current flows through the circuit the fuse melts and breaks the circuit.

9.2.1 Types of fuse

Rewirable fuses are still to be found in older houses. They consist of tinned copper wire of a diameter dependent upon their current rating. They are open to abuse, since the householder may replace blown fuse wire with too great a rated wire.

Cartridge fuses consist of a wire element encased in a cartridge that is filled with particles of sand or a similar material. The wire element is secured to metal caps at each end. These are easier to replace and react faster than rewirable fuses. This type of fuse is also found in plugs. To aid identification cartridge fuses are colour coded.

Miniature circuit breakers (MCBs) are provided in most new houses. A switch is turned off in the consumer unit if a fault occurs. These are more expensive but are more reliable and quicker to respond to a fault.

9.2.2 Earthing

The function of earthing is to act as a safety device to prevent electrocution. If a live wire comes into contact with a metal object then anyone touching that object will receive an electric shock as the electricity flows through the person's body to the ground. To avoid this, metal parts of electrical appliances should be connected to earth by means of an earth wire. Thus the electricity will flow through the earth wire rather than through the person. As this occurs the amount of current flowing through the circuit increases, which will blow a fuse or trip a miniature circuit breaker. The earth terminal is normally provided by the electricity company close to its sealed fuse.

Methods of earthing are as follows.

Old houses
The earthing was commonly carried out by connection to the cold water rising main. This is not recommended nowadays as the water main may be in plastic pipework.

Protective multiple earthing (PME)
This is the system used in most new houses. The neutral pole of mains electricity is connected to earth at the substation and provides a good earth. The neutral conductor of the supply network is therefore used as the earth return path as well as performing its normal function of carrying current. The protective metal sheath of the mains cable is connected to the earth wire.

Earth rods
Where the protective metal sheath of the earth wire is not continuous, or in areas where PME has not yet been implemented, earthing can be ensured via a copper stake driven into the ground. This method is not as good, as it is affected by the type of soil, its firmness and water content. If used it is usually with a back-up device such as an earth leakage circuit breaker.

Earth leakage circuit breaker (ELCB) residual current device
Similar to (but not to be confused with) MCBs, these are found in the consumer unit rather than the mains switch. They monitor the amount of current entering and leaving a circuit. If the two are not the same the difference must have leaked to earth, and the ELCB 'trips off'. ELCBs are very sensitive, and their reaction time is very short.

Bonding
In order to prevent metal surrounds that might accidentally come into contact with an electrical current from causing electrocution it is necessary for these to be bonded: that is, connected to the main earth terminal. Since a wet body is less resistant to shock, bonding is particularly important in bathrooms and shower-rooms.

9.2.3 Wiring and fittings

The inspection of wiring and fittings gives the biggest clue to the likely age and condition of the installation.

The main wiring carrying the supply to the outlets is referred to as a *cable*, and consists of conducting wires and protective insulation. The conductors are usually made from copper (although sometimes aluminium is used). The rating is based on the cross-sectional area of the wires: for example, a power ring circuit may be rated as 2.5 mm². Cables with a cross-sectional area of 2.5 mm² are single stranded, but above this size they are usually made up of multiple strands of copper. The earth conductor is slightly smaller than the other two as it carries a load only when there is a fault. Circuits carrying a heavy current, such as a cooker, have a rating of 6–10 mm².

The insulating material around the wires is usually PVC, as is the sheathing around the cable. PVC is used because it is relatively tough, incombustible and inert, and it does not deteriorate with age, although it does soften at temperatures around 70°C. PVC is suitable for burying in most plasters. Mineral-insulated, metal-sheathed cable is rarely used in housing because of its high cost. PVC cable has been used for about the last 35 years, but before this cloth-covered, rubber-insulated cable was used. The rubber was prone to perishing, leading to short-circuits and possible fires. In even older (pre-Second World War) properties lead-sheathed cable may be found. The actual wires were insulated with rubber, and the lead sheathing acted as an earth: there were dangers with earthing arrangements being compromised if the lead was damaged.

Anything other than PVC-sheathed cable will have reached the end of its life, and some early PVC-cabled installations will also be nearing the ends of their lives. The IEE recommends that installations be tested every 5 years, and even if the surveyor's visual inspection reveals no problems the advice about regular testing should be passed on to the client.

Socket outlets have also changed over the years. Early sockets were of two-pin type: these lacked earth protection, and there were no fuses in the plugs. In the 1930s these were replaced with round three-pin sockets, which were earthed but still lacked fuses. The modern square-pin, 13-amp sockets have been used since the 1950s but when inspecting houses it should be realised that these may be connected to old wiring.

Cables can be laid in conduits or trunking. *Conduit* consists of metal or PVC tubes that protect cables from being damaged. Cables can be withdrawn without affecting the finishes of the building. *Trunking* performs a similar function but provides continuous access to the cable. It is usual to bury cables below the wall surface, and this is best done by cutting a chase in the masonry so that the cable is protected by the full thickness of the plaster. Cables should only be run vertically down walls, and horizontal runs should be contained in floor or ceiling voids. In addition:

- Joists should be drilled a minimum of 50 mm below the surface to avoid nail damage.

- Cables should be fixed to joists where running parallel to them, and should not be run diagonally across floors or ceiling, bent sharply or fixed to the top of ceiling joists in roof spaces.
- Cables passing through masonry walls should be protected by conduit.
- Contact between PVC cables and cement, polystyrene and water should be avoided.
- Cables should not be allowed to overheat, for example by being in contact with hot water cylinders. Cables can also overheat if covered with roof insulation, and wiring should be above and not below the insulation.

Defects in electrical installations are obviously very serious because of the safety implications. In addition to matters raised above, common defects are:

- overloading the circuit by using socket adapters
- replacing fuse wire with wire of the incorrect rating, or wire not intended for the purpose (the author has witnessed a former paper-clip used as 'fuse wire' for a lighting circuit)
- substituting metal elements for non-metal elements without attending to earthing arrangements – for example replacing plastic switches and ceiling roses with brass ones
- using lightswitches rather than pull cords in bathrooms, where people are likely to touch the switch with a wet hand
- running a spur off a spur
- loose connections in the plug or socket (this can cause overheating and scorching)
- using lightbulbs that have too high a wattage for the lightshade
- rodent damage to wiring.[3]

9.3   Heating and associated installations

Identify the type, age and general condition of the heating source. To include ventilation and siting requirements and flue condition where visible and appropriate.

Locate and identify the heating control system including programmers, thermostats, valves and controllers.

Identify and inspect a sample of the pipework, heat emitters and associated appliances (including water storage tanks) to allow a general assessment of condition and suitability without any form of test.

Identify any obvious hazards or safety issues associated with the heating installation.

In urban locations the most common fuel used by heating appliances is mains gas, but where this is not available (or where the building owner has a prejudice against gas) oil, liquefied petroleum gas (lpg) or solid fuel may be used. Alternatively off-peak electrical heating may be installed. We shall first consider wet heating systems.

A visual inspection of the boiler should be carried out and an estimate of its age made. In many cases a history of recent service work is fixed either onto the boiler itself or in a nearby position. If there is no evidence of a recent service having been carried out then the client should be advised of this fact. Ventilation arrangements for the conventional flued heating appliance should be checked. There should be a permanent ventilation opening, of at least the same size as the flue, provided close to the boiler. Where the appliance has a balanced flue the surveyor should check that this is no closer than 600 mm to a window or door, that it is guarded, and that it is unobstructed (for example by vegetation). The proximity of combustible material to the balanced flue should also be checked; it is not uncommon for the flue to be located too close to PVC rainwater goods, causing them to deform. A heat shield should be provided if the flue is closer than 1 m to combustible material.

The type of heating system should then be ascertained: is it a *vented* or *unvented* system? The latter operates at mains pressure, and there will be no feed and expansion (or header) tank, which is usually located in the roof space. Water by-laws have permitted unvented systems in the UK only for the last 10 years or so, and so such systems are likely to be relatively modern and must have been installed by a British Board of Agrément certified contractor. Safety devices including an expansion vessel are required with an unvented system, and in hard water areas the surveyor will need to check that a water softener is provided to prevent furring of the boiler.

Modern wet central heating systems (whether vented or unvented) will all have a flow and return pipe connecting the boiler to the radiators, but older systems may only have a single pipe acting as both flow and return. The one-pipe system was fairly common in houses built during the 1960s and 1970s, and the author has recently inspected a house that still has its original one-pipe system. The obvious disadvantage of such a system is that in use the radiators furthest from the boiler are a good deal colder than those closest to it. If both flow and return valves are connected to the same pipe then the system is a one-pipe type.

The use of microbore pipework has become quite common in recent years, particularly in refurbishment work where there is limited space to accommodate the usual 15–22 mm diameter flow and return pipework. Such a system uses a manifold that has traditional-sized flow and return pipes running from it to the boiler, but there are 8, 10 or 12 mm diameter pipes running from the manifold to the radiators. The use of special double-entry valves at one side of the radiator only is fairly common with microbore installations. The disadvantages of such installations are that the smaller and softer pipes are more prone to blockage and are more easily damaged.

When inspecting a wet central heating system it should be switched on even if the inspection is carried out in the middle of summer. Obviously the owner's consent is required to use the fuel that they are paying for, and there must be fuel available. If for any reason it is not possible to operate the heating system then the client should be advised of this fact. It will be appreciated that the radiators will take some time to heat up, and this aspect of the inspection should not be left until the end of the visit. All radiators should be checked to ensure that they are warm, and valves should be turned to make sure that they are not stuck (most modern systems have thermostatically controlled valves, and if these do not operate then it will not be possible to control the system). Evidence of corrosion to radiators should be looked for, as well as possible leaks. If there are cold spots at the top of radiators then this suggests air locks, and the client should be advised that the system requires bleeding. However, if there are cold spots on the bottom of radiators this suggests that there is sludge in the radiators. This is a result of corrosion within the system as a result of air gaining entry, and remedial work including the removal of the sludge and the use of a corrosion inhibitor within the header tank should be advised.

The header tank should be inspected for the existence of a cover, insulation and an overflow pipe. Most modern tanks will be of plastic, but if there are older galvanised steel or asbestos tanks the client should be advised that these require replacement. All pipework associated with the heating system should be lagged where it is located in unheated areas.

When inspecting dry heating systems there is little that can be checked, particularly if the inspection is carried out in the summer months when the installation is not in operation. Since such systems use off-peak electricity the surveyor will not be able to switch on the system. In such cases all the surveyor can do is comment on such things as the age of the electric storage heaters.

9.4   Plumbing installations

Identify whether the water has mains or private supply and assess whether the provision is suitable within the context of the type of property and its location.

Locate the stopcock and assess general condition.

Identify and inspect a sample of the pipework, control valves, water storage tanks and other associated appliances and fixtures where visible for condition and suitability without any special test.

Inspect kitchen and sanitary fittings to assess their general condition.

Identify any obvious hazards or safety issues associated with the plumbing installation.

If there is a private supply then laboratory testing of the water should be recommended. The type of cold water installation should be ascertained: it will either be direct off the mains or indirect (incorporating a cold water storage cistern, probably located in the roof space). The obvious disadvantage of a direct supply is that there are no storage facilities available should the mains supply be disconnected for any period.

The stopcock will probably be located beneath the kitchen sink in a modern property but in a property built before the Second World War may be located in the understairs cupboard or even beneath a ground floorboard (usually just inside the front door). In some even older properties there may not be an internal stopcock, and it will be located in a box in the garden or front path. The material of the rising main should be identified. In most modern properties the pipework will be of polythene, but in older properties it may be in lead, in which case the health hazards should be advised to the client (see section 9.9 below). The stopcock should be operated to ensure that it does disconnect the supply of water to the property.

The position of the cold water storage cistern should be located and its type and condition ascertained. In most cases the tank is to be found in the roof space, and the method of support should be checked to ensure that there is no overloading of the roof structure. As before, if the tank is of asbestos cement or galvanised steel then its replacement should be recommended. Lagging of the tank and pipework should be verified, together with the presence of a cover and overflow. The roof insulation should not be carried under the cistern.

The hot water storage tank or cylinder should be located and its type noted. The use of any electric immersion heaters should be recorded. Most modern cylinders have two heaters fitted, one connected to the off-peak supply (for use during the summer months when hot water for heating is not required) and the other connected to the normal supply for boost purposes only. Off-peak electricity is the least expensive method of heating hot water when the boiler is not being used for central heating. An insulation jacket of at least 40 mm thickness should be provided, and in modern systems the presence of a thermostat should be verified.

The type of hot and cold water distribution pipework should be noted: in most cases it will be copper, but plastic pipework is increasingly being used in new houses. If there is any lead pipework present then the client should be advised to replace this as soon as possible.

The type, location and general condition of kitchen and sanitary fittings should be noted. If the kitchen units are the cheapest self-assembly type then the client must not be left under the impression that they are of the highest quality. Sanitary fittings should be carefully inspected to ensure that they are not chipped or cracked. Are the WC seats attached to the pans?

Mechanical ventilation of bathrooms and kitchens should be checked. Leaks from sanitary fittings should be looked for, and the surveyor should check that all the WC cisterns have an overflow properly connected.

9.5   Underground drainage systems

Identify the type of underground drainage installation and sewerage disposal system to assess its suitability within the context of the type of property and its location.

Locate the inspection chambers, cesspits and septic tanks and lift light and accessible covers.

Inspect internally and assess suitability.

Identify the route of the underground drain runs where possible and identify and assess any potential defects without any special test.

Identify and assess the suitability and condition of visible gullies.

Identify any obvious hazards or safety issues associated with the underground drainage system.

The drainage will be connected to one of four systems:

- *separate foul and combined sewers* – most usual in modern-day developments, particularly in urban locations
- *foul water sewer with surface water to soakaways* – mainly in semi-rural locations (there is a variant of this system, where surface water drainage at

the front of the property is to the surface water sewer serving the road, but there are soakaways at the rear)
- *combined foul and surface water sewers* – common in urban locations, particularly older properties
- *private treatment installation (cesspit or septic tank)* – in rural locations where no mains drainage is available.

The surveyor should raise any inspection chamber cover that is capable of being raised by one person with reasonable effort, and run water through system(s) to ensure that no blockages are evident, recording the location and severity of any blockages. The position of any solids within the system should also be noted. From the condition of the drains visible within the chambers an assessment should be made of the likely age of the system (has it been renewed since construction of the building?). If the jointing between channels in the chamber is in poor condition then it is possible that the joints between sections of drain are in a similar condition. Where alterations have been made, have branches been connected at benching level? It is much easier for the builder to connect new branches at a higher level, but this will probably lead to blockages. If the walls of the interior of the chamber are rendered the condition of the rendering should be noted. In pre-Second World War properties it was common to fit interceptor traps to the chamber nearest the sewer, but such traps are often the cause of blockages. If such a trap is fitted, the presence of the cover to the rodding eye should be noted: if it is missing rats can enter the drains of the property.

Cesspits are tanks that have sufficient capacity to store a minimum of 45 days' effluent and which therefore require emptying several times a year – at an annual cost of several thousand pounds. Septic tanks on the other hand treat the effluent by biological action before the 'clean' water is disposed of to a watercourse or soakaway. The permission of the National Rivers Authority is required for this discharge, and in certain sensitive environmental areas (such as in parts of the Norfolk Broads) such discharge is not permitted and a full-scale private treatment works is then required. It is recommended that a septic tank be desludged every 6 months. Older tanks usually consist of two brick chambers, but modern tanks consist of an onion-shaped glass-reinforced plastic vessel. It is impossible from a simple visual inspection to determine that either a cesspit or septic tank is operating satisfactorily and one family's production of effluent may be very different from another's. The advice should always be given to clients when inspecting private treatment installations that it is possible to assess the efficiency of a private installation only through use over a period of time.

It is usually impossible to locate surface water soakaways, unless they have caused some settlement of the garden above them. They should be sited at least 4.5 m from any building. Usually rainwater downpipes are not provided with gullies when they are connected to soakaways, so that the only way to carry out any form of water runaway test is from a paving gulley.

Rainwater downpipes must be connected to a gulley if the drainage installation is of a combined type.

As well as inspecting those parts of the system to which access is available it will be necessary to make an assessment of the likely condition of other parts. Where there is cracking to adjacent walls and/or pavings or where there has been some settlement of pavings then leaking drains are a possible cause. If there is any doubt about the watertightness of the installation, a test should be recommended. For additional advice about drain testing see Chapter 4.

9.6   Above-ground drainage and rainwater systems

Identify the type of above-ground drainage installation (including guttering and rainwater pipes) and assess its suitability for the type of property.

Locate the main stack pipe, branch connections and other associated fittings and appliances and assess their suitability without any special tests.

Locate and assess the condition of visible waste traps and fittings and appliances and assess their suitability without any special test.

Locate and assess the condition of visible gutters and rainwater downpipes and assess their suitability without any special test.

Identify any obvious hazards or safety issues associated with the above-ground drainage system.

The two-pipe plumbing system will generally be found in houses dating from the 1920s until the 1950s, provided that this has not been updated. One pipe carries the soil water from the WC and the other carries the waste water from the bath and basin. On many houses the waste pipe also carries water from the roof. The system worked well as the combination of waste and rainwater flushed the system. However, a weak point is the hopper head, which blocks with waste products and leaves, and this should be checked (it is usually possible to do this from the bathroom window).

The one-pipe system was introduced during the 1950s as a result of design work by the BRE. A single stack carries soil and waste water, but in order to prevent trap siphonage there are restrictions on the length and gradient of branch drain runs, which the surveyor should check:

- bath and sink – maximum branch drain length 3 m for a 40 mm pipe, slope 18–90 mm depending on length
- wash basin – maximum length 1.7 m for a 32 mm pipe
- WC – 6 m maximum for 100 mm pipe, slope minimum 18 mm per m.

In addition, where the waste branch is below the WC branch it should be a minimum of 200 mm below to prevent WC soil water backing up the waste branch. The distance between the lowest connection and the drain invert must be at least 450 mm, otherwise the fitting must be connected to the below-ground drainage system. There must be a large-radius bend to connect the stack to the drain, and the top of the stack must vent to the external air and be well clear of any window opening. The alternative is to provide an air admittance valve at the top of the pipe. This allows air in but will not allow any air (and therefore smells) out and may be located in, for example, the roof space. Single stacks can be used externally on buildings up to three storeys high, but above this height the stack must be located internally so that easy access to it is available. On commercial buildings for which the design criteria of the single-stack system cannot be met, the surveyor should be expecting to find a separate ventilation system to ensure that trap siphonage does not occur.

When inspecting above-ground drainage the essential matters to be checked are for any signs of leaks and that there is adequate support of branch drains. When inspecting rainwater goods during dry weather then signs of leaks should be looked for. Very often white and green staining will be evident on the underside of gutters, at joints, suggesting that these are not watertight (if there is paving immediately beneath the guttering there may even be staining on this). Downpipes should be checked for any sign of blockage or leakage, paying particular attention to the rear of the pipe. Most modern-day rainwater goods are in plastic, and the support of gutters in particular should be checked. Cast-iron rainwater goods should be checked for any sign of corrosion, and downpipes should be tapped with a small metal object. If they are watertight there is a high-pitched note, but a much duller or deader sound is heard if they are not. It is also often possible to hear rust falling down the inside of the pipe when carrying out this operation. During the periods when plastic replaced cast iron, asbestos cement rainwater goods were used. The joints of any remaining asbestos cement gutters are unlikely to be watertight, the material is very brittle and susceptible to impact damage, and there are of course health problems associated with asbestos (see section 9.9 below).

9.7 Gas installations and oil storage

Locate and identify the nature of the gas or oil supply (e.g. natural gas or liquefied petroleum gas, heating oil tank) and assess its suitability.

Locate the bulk storage container, gas meter and control valve and assess their suitability.

Identify and inspect a sample of pipework, control valves, and associated appliances, etc. where visible for condition, presence of ventilation and suitability without any special test.

Identify any obvious hazards or safety issues associated with the gas installation.

Where gas is used the position of the gas meter should be located and noted. Where material is stored then the receptacle should be inspected and its condition noted. Most oil storage is now in plastic tanks, but where an old steel tank remains this should be carefully inspected for corrosion, paying particular attention to the underside of the tank. The level of oil or gas in the tank should be recorded.

9.8   Other services

Locate and identify any other services that exist within the property (e.g. fire alarms, security installations, CCTV).

Perhaps the most common item to be inspected is the security system, but for obvious reasons most owners are averse to actually demonstrating this. If this is the case then the client should be advised accordingly. However, basic details such as the location of sensors and whether the system is linked to any external monitoring system should be noted.

9.9   Environmental issues

Harmful substances

The surveyor will inspect for visual signs of contamination by harmful substances but will not research the presence or possible consequences of these factors. Typical contaminants in this context include:

- *asbestos*
- *high-voltage electrical supply equipment*
- *lead*
- *mining (in known areas a mining search is recommended)*
- *proximity to land waste sites, current or former (if in the public domain or on a public register)*
- *proximity to chemical or other plants with noxious or unpleasant smells.*

A noticeable exception to this list is radon. In areas of high incidence of radon gas it would be appropriate for the surveyor to advise for the need for measurement and possible remedial measures. See reference 4 for guidance from the National Radiological Protection Board and the BRE on the measurement of radon and on remedial measures.

If asbestos products are identified, an assessment will be required of what risk these present. In general, loose fibrous materials such as lagging present far more of a risk than asbestos cement components in good condition. If in doubt it is best to advise that specialist advice be sought, and if removal is required then this must be undertaken by a licensed contractor.

Recent studies have indicated that there is a slightly increased risk of cancer in children if they live close to overhead power cables. If the property is located close to such power lines then the client must be advised of the slight potential risk. Similarly there is also a slight risk if the property is close to land waste sites.

As indicated above (section 9.4), because of the dangers of lead poisoning the client should be advised to remove any lead plumbing. Where, however, the water main is still in lead pipework then the recommendation should be that the water company be asked to measure the lead content of the water. If this is high then the company has a duty to replace the main up to the customer's stopcock.

If the surveyor suspects that the building has been built on, or is close to contaminated land then the client should be advised that this could have a serious impact upon the value of the property. Of course if the surveyor is unaware that the contaminated land exists then he or she is at a serious disadvantage. This is yet another reason for the advice given in section 4.1 that surveyors should survey buildings only in geographical areas with which they are familiar.

9.10   Insulation

Thermal insulation

The surveyor will identify so far as is possible the levels of thermal insulation in the dwelling. This will normally include:

- *roof and wall insulation*
- *double glazing*
- *floor insulation*

- *draught stripping*
- *insulation to plumbing, heating pipes and tanks.*

The extent of this inspection will often be restricted, as much insulation in a dwelling will be concealed within the construction.

This benchmark statement is fairly straightforward. Any divergence from good levels of thermal insulation should be reported to the client. The preliminary version of the home condition report (produced by DETR before the Homes Bill fell) suggests that the Government may require a full Standard Assessment Procedure (SAP) rating to be calculated. This task is quite demanding (and will therefore be expensive for the client). If the legislation is resurrected it may be that this aspect of the new report is challenged following consultation with the surveying professions.

Sound insulation

The surveyor will identify the apparent levels of sound insulation in the dwelling. This will normally include checking:

- *between neighbouring properties*
- *to the external walls and windows and external noise sources.*

The extent of this inspection will often be restricted, as much insulation in a dwelling will be concealed within the construction.

Obviously this applies only to dwellings that are linked vertically or horizontally to another. In modern properties the levels of insulation are likely to be good, but in older dwellings they may be very poor. In one town in which the author has practised it was not uncommon for the party walls between terraced houses to be only half a brick thick. Brickwork only 100 mm thick obviously provides very poor sound insulation. If there is any concern about levels of insulation, it is appropriate to advise for a building services engineer to carry out acoustic tests – although of course the adjoining owner would need to consent to these. If the building is in an area where high noise levels are encountered, this should always be pointed out to the client – just in case he hasn't noticed!

9.11 Summary

At present the UK surveyor is required only to inspect service installations and not to test them. If we are to follow the example of US home inspectors then this may change at some time in the future. In any event the surveyor must be extremely thorough in the inspection of the electrical, plumbing and drainage installations and in the assessment of environmental matters. In the next chapter, the final one about the inspection, those matters that have not so far been considered are discussed.

Notes

1 SAVA *Benchmark Standards for the Homebuyer Survey and Valuation* (Surveyors and Valuers Accreditation, Woking, 2000).

2 P. Parnham and C. Rispin *Residential Property Appraisal*, pp 229–230 (Spon Press, London, 2001).

3 D. Marshall and D. Worthing *The Construction of Houses* (Estates Gazette, London, 2000).

4 D.W. Dixon and C. Scivyer 'Radon and remedial measures' *Structural Survey*, Vol. 17 (1999), No. 3, pp 154–159.

10   The inspection: other matters

10.1   Introduction

Those elements of a survey that result in most negligence claims have been considered in Chapter 8, followed by services and environmental matters in Chapter 9. The secondary or slightly less 'risky' items are considered in this chapter. These items still require the same degree of professional care when carrying out the inspection.

10.2   External joinery and decorations

Wet rot has been considered in Chapter 8, and where there is painted softwood external joinery this is the main concern. However, hardwood, plastic and metal frames also require careful inspection. Even where there are non-softwood windows and doors there may be softwood roof fascia, soffit and barge boards, and these will require careful inspection, including probing at susceptible locations such as the bottom of barge boards. Where such locations are beyond the reach of the standard length of a surveyor's ladder then inspection should be made by binoculars. Similar comments apply to any horizontal or vertical timber cladding to walls.

Metal windows such as those manufactured by the Essex based company Crittal are still in existence, particularly in local authority houses built during the 1950s and 1960s. Common problems with these are distorted frames and excessive condensation. Some sliding aluminium windows installed in 1970s-built houses have poor serviceability and, because they were only single glazed, suffer from condensation. All casements and sashes should be checked to ensure that they open and close satisfactorily. The fashion for uPVC replacement windows shows little sign of abating, and when inspecting these the following should be considered:

- the quality of product and installation
- whether there is an insurance-backed guarantee available
- whether adequate natural light and ventilation are provided to habitable rooms.

All double-glazed sealed units should be checked to ensure that no condensation is occurring between the panes as a result of defective edge seals. Most good quality double-glazed sealed units have a 10-year guarantee.

Security should also be considered when inspecting windows and external doors. The adequacy of window locks and the existence of mortise deadlocks to doors should be checked.

The estimated life to the next external redecoration should be noted. Any onerous maintenance liabilities such as extensive areas of painted walls or cladding should be recorded.

10.3   Internal walls and partitions

By examining the layout of upper floor walls, floor joist directions and any intermediate support to the roof structure, the surveyor should determine which internal walls are load-bearing. Structural problems affecting only the internal walls are not uncommon, particularly in pre-Second World War properties, in which foundations to internal walls were frequently shallower and less substantial than those to the external walls. Of course, where floor joists run front to rear and a roof purlin also struts onto the main cross-wall, this wall carries twice the vertical loads imposed on the external walls. As mentioned in Chapter 8, clients of the author awoke one night to discover that their bed was sliding across the upper floor bedroom. A burst water main beneath the sand subsoil had caused the foundation to the main cross-wall to subside, causing extensive damage to the partition itself and also to the floor and roof structures that it supported. Sloping floors and distorted door openings are indications of less significant but still serious structural movement of load-bearing internal walls. A spirit level should be used to check for these tell-tale signs. Internal door openings should be inspected carefully by opening and closing all doors, and any signs of recent easing of doors should be noted.

Some 20 years ago there was a fashion in new speculative housing for supporting concrete blockwork partitions off doubled-up timber floor joists. While it was possible to prove by calculation that the timber beam was capable of carrying the load, sometimes excessive drying shrinkage of the joists caused significant deflection to occur. This defect very often manifests itself by cracking between the first floor partition and the ceiling and by some distortion of adjacent door openings.

Another method of construction that has become fashionable in speculative housing over the last 20 years is the use of very lightweight plasterboard partitions where these are non-load-bearing. Such partitions have relatively poor sound insulation and low impact damage resistance, and are unable to support heavy fixings: this should be pointed out to clients purchasing such properties.

The state of internal decoration should be recorded and a general comment provided in the report. Of course, many purchasers prefer to completely redecorate their new property. However, any dangerous materials (such as polystyrene ceiling tiles) or decorations that may be expensive to replace (such as Artexed walls) should be reported upon.

10.4 Floors

The most serious defects likely to affect suspended timber ground and first floors (fungal attack and insect infestation) have been considered in Chapter 8. The importance of checking for adequate sub-floor ventilation in suspended timber ground floors cannot be emphasized enough. In most older properties the current Building Regulations requirement of one 225 × 150 mm airbrick every 1500 mm is unlikely to be satisfied. What should be looked for are enough airbricks to ensure a through flow of air beneath the floor. Where extensions with solid floors have been built at the rear of properties with suspended timber ground floors, evidence of ducting to adequately vent what is now an internal floor void should be looked for.

It is necessary to raise one floorboard at each floor level in order to assess conditions within the sub-floor void. Fixed boards should be raised for a full building survey, but the surveyor is required only to raise loose boards when undertaking the intermediate-level inspection. In most Victorian and Edwardian properties there is a loose floorboard where the cold water rising main enters, usually just inside the front door or in the understairs cupboard, and this is the most convenient position at which to inspect the ground floor void (with the aid of a small mirror and a torch). The existence of a concrete sub-floor, any build-up of debris or dampness in the void, adequate honeycombing of sleeper walls and the presence of damp-proof courses between wall plate and sleeper wall can usually be checked by an inspection from a single point.

All suspended timber floors should be checked for excessive deflection by jumping up and down on them. Where there is excessive deflection then problems should be anticipated and further investigation should be recommended.

Solid ground floors should be checked for signs of settlement or heave. Heave may be the result of sulphate attack or caused by swelling of hardcore additives or a clay subsoil (usually following removal of vegetation: see Chapter 8). Settlement is usually caused by failure to adequately compact the hardcore or by subsidence of the subsoil. Table 10.1 reproduced from BRE Digest 251 indicates the typical signs of a solid concrete floor suffering from settlement and provides a method of classifying the damage caused.[1] The main signs of a heaving floor are doors catching on the floor and a clear rise in the level of the floor slab at some point. In extreme cases the external walls are pushed outwards by the swelling floor and there is slippage of the walls at dpc level.

Table 10.1 Classification of visible damage caused by ground floor slab settlement

Damage category	Description of typical damage	Approximate (a) crack width (b) gap*
0	Hairline cracks between floor and skirtings.	(a) NA (b) Up to 1 mm
1	Settlement of the floor slab, either at a corner or along a short wall, or possibly uniformly, such that a gap opens up below skirting boards that can be masked by resetting skirting boards. No cracks in walls. No cracks in floor slab, although there may be negligible cracks in floor screed and finish. Slab reasonably level.	(a) NA (b) Up to 6 mm
2	Larger gaps below skirting boards, some obvious but limited local settlement leading to a slight slope of floor slab; gaps can be masked by resetting skirting boards, and some local rescreeding may be necessary. Fine cracks appear in internal partition walls, which need some redecoration; slight distortion in door frames so some 'jamming' may occur, necessitating adjustment of doors. No cracks in floor slab although there may be very slight cracks in floor screed and finish. Slab reasonably level.	(a) Up to 1 mm (b) Up to 13 mm
3	Significant gaps below skirting boards with areas of floor, especially at corners or ends, where local settlements may have caused slight cracking of floor slab. Sloping of floor in these areas is clearly visible (slope approximately 1 in 150). Some disruption to drain, plumbing or heating pipes may occur. Damage to internal walls is more widespread, with some crack filling or replastering of partitions necessary. Doors may have to be refitted. Inspection reveals some voids below slab with poor or loosely compacted fill.	(a) Up to 5 mm (b) Up to 19 mm

Table 10.1 Classification of visible damage caused by ground floor slab settlement
– *continued*

Damage category	Description of typical damage	Approximate (a) crack width (b) gap*
4	Large, localised gaps below skirting boards; possibly some cracks in floor slab with sharp fall to edge of slab (slope approximately 1 in 500 or more). Inspection reveals voids exceeding 50 mm below slab and/or poor or loose fill likely to settle further. Local breaking-out, part refilling and relaying of floor slab or grouting of fill may be necessary; damage to internal partitions may require replacement of some bricks or blocks or relining of stud partitions.	(a) 5–15 mm but may also depend on number of cracks (b) Up to 25 mm
5	Either very large, overall floor settlement with large movement of walls and damage at junctions extending up to first-floor area, with possible damage to exterior walls, or large differential settlements across floor slab. Voids exceeding 75 mm below slab and/or very poor or very loose fill likely to settle further. Risk of instability. Most or all of floor slab requires breaking out and relaying or grouting of fill; internal partitions need replacement.	(a) Usually greater than 15 mm but depends on number of cracks (b) Greater than 25 mm

*'Gap' refers to space – usually between the skirting and finished floor – caused by settlement after making appropriate allowance for discrepancy in building, shrinkage, normal bedding and the like.
Source: Based on Table 2 of BRE Digest 251:1995. Reproduced by permission of BRE.

The other main concern with a ground floor solid floor is the adequacy of the damp-proof membrane. A moisture meter is essential for the determination of any damp defects, and as well as high readings on the floor surface, high readings may be obtained in skirting boards and in the wall plaster immediately above skirting board level.

The main concern with suspended timber upper floors – apart from woodworm infestation – is their structural adequacy. In poorer quality speculative housing of the Georgian and later periods very slender joists were sometimes used, particularly in rear additions, and these are prone to deflection and in a few cases total failure. Again the main way to test all suspended timber floors is to jump up and down on them. In some properties built during the second half of the last century suspended concrete floor slabs will be encountered, particularly in blocks of flats. Structural problems with such floors are not common, but the surveyor should be alert to the possible use of high-alumina cement (HAC) in their construction if built before the mid 1970s. Concrete using HAC can deteriorate rapidly (and in extreme cases fail) in warm and humid conditions. See reference 2 for the latest BRE guidance on the assessment of ageing HAC concrete.

10.5   Ceilings

While some assessment of the condition of ceilings is possible from an inspection of their underside it is possible to determine the type (and therefore the potential problems with) the ceiling only following an inspection from above. This can be accomplished on the top floor from within the roof space but at lower floor levels it is necessary to raise a floorboard. In domestic situations the material used almost exclusively for ceilings since the period between the two World Wars is of course plasterboard. Generally this material suffers little from defects unless it becomes wet. If affected by roof or plumbing leaks plasterboard is likely to require replacement. Of course the material will not support very much weight from above, and any excessive storage in roof spaces should be noted and reported upon. Other potential problems are associated with poor-quality workmanship. The lack of noggins at joints between boards, the use of nails that are too short and the use of board of inadequate thickness can all lead to problems. A client of the author's required the complete replacement of the ceiling of his new bungalow where the builder had tried to save money by using 9 mm plasterboard (instead of the 12 mm specified) to span between trussed rafters spaced 600 mm apart.

Before the introduction of plasterboard the most common type of ceiling was of course lath and plaster: three coats of lime plaster applied to thin strips of softwood. Such ceilings are prone to failure as a result of the plaster losing key, rot or insect attack to the laths, and water damage. Any property discovered to have lath and plaster ceilings is likely to require new ceilings within the foreseeable future. Indications of imminent failure are ceilings that are bulging or excessively cracked. The author practised for many years in an area close to the Norfolk Broads, and in this area it was common to find reed and plaster ceilings. These suffer from similar problems to lath and plaster ceilings and generally have a lower life expectancy.

10.6 Staircases

The condition both of the staircase itself (that is, treads, risers and strings) and of balustrades and handrails should be noted. Woodworm infestation of older staircases is quite common, and rot should be checked for where the stairs adjoin an external wall. Obviously the full requirements of the current Building Regulations are unlikely to be complied with, but any design issue that is seriously short of modern standards will need to be commented upon. If for example the headroom over one flight is low then a tall client is likely to take exception if this fact has not been pointed out in the survey report. Items that have an impact upon safety, such as narrow winding treads, or balustrades with ranch-style bars or with any large openings, should be particularly highlighted.

10.7 Internal doors

The type of door in each room should be recorded, together with a note of its condition. As indicated above, every door should be opened and closed, paying particular attention to the head of the opening. Any distortion in this position is a likely indication of structural movement. Attention should also be paid to the bottom of the doors to ensure that there are no excessive gaps beneath them: the author once inspected a bungalow the internal doors of which had 50 mm gaps beneath them! The condition of ironmongery should be recorded. When inspecting properties requiring a fire certificate many doors will of course need to be fire doors (this also applies in some domestic situations – for example between an integral garage and the dwelling). The operation of door closers should be checked, and the depth of rebates should also be verified when inspecting fire doors.

10.8 Fireplaces and chimney-stacks

Great care is required in inspecting any property that has chimney-stacks, and the surveyor should ensure sufficient time is devoted to fully inspect all aspects of the stack. The difficulty of course is that the various components of the stack are to be found in several different locations, but to miss one small piece of evidence can lead to errors occurring. When inspecting the exterior the number and locations of stacks should be recorded; the author has always found it useful to do this by adding them to the roof plan that is drawn during the early stages of the inspection (see Chapter 7). The number of flues should be recorded, together with the condition of the brickwork and flashings. The folly of rendering brick chimney-stacks above roof level should be reported to the client if appropriate.

The next careful inspection required is in the roof space, where the existence of the chimneys should be verified and a note of the condition recorded, paying particular attention to any evidence of rain penetration – with the aid of a moisture meter. The rendering of the stack in a roof space is a common position for the builder to have engraved the date of construction. Any support of chimney-breast brickwork at or just above the upper floor level should be noted. Then in each room the existence of the chimney-breast should be verified, and where it is missing, the method of support should be ascertained. If any brickwork is supported off ceiling or floor joists then the need for re-support, using steelwork, should be reported to the client.

Where flues are no longer used then ventilation of these should be verified (and recommended where it is missing). Where there are fireplaces evident the flue should be inspected with the aid of a small mirror and a torch. Where brick flues are not lined then the possible need for lining in the future should be reported. Where there are conventional flued heating appliances making use of any chimney-stack flues then an appropriately sited ventilation opening of at least the size of the flue should be checked for and recommended if missing. The existence of a standard flue liner terminal at roof level suggests that the flue has been lined, but is not of course certain evidence that the flue has been *satisfactorily* lined. Where there is a statutory need for monitoring of heating appliances (such as in houses in multiple occupation), a carbon monoxide test should be carried out or recommended.

Particular care should be taken to record any evidence of dampness to chimney-breasts. However, the diagnosis of the causes of such dampness is not always straightforward. Sometimes the dampness is the result of a defective flashing, but it can also be coming from within the flue, as a result either of condensation of flue gases or of rain penetration (sometimes soot deposits in the flue can exaggerate the latter problem). It can take some time and expense to remedy chimney-stack dampness problems, and the client should be put on notice of this fact.

10.9   Unwelcome visitors

Humans are not the only creatures who will take up occupation of buildings, and – if given the opportunity – there are innumerable unwelcome visitors that the surveyor must be alert to discovering and advising his client about. Where dogs and cats also occupy dwellings then it is possible that fleas will also take up residence. In hot weather, what started off as a few fleas can quickly develop into an epidemic, and a new owner would need to fumigate all carpets before taking up occupation. Even if the surveyor does not see any evidence of rats or mice, he may see traps that have been left for these rodents – particularly in roof spaces. The surveyor should then report that rodents have probably been a problem in the past.

Squirrels will also enter buildings, particularly when looking for somewhere to hibernate. Bats are of course protected by statute, and if encountered (usually in the roof space) should not be disturbed. Piles of droppings and discarded insect wings are usually the first signs of the presence of bats in a roof space. Any woodworm or rot eradication treatments necessary to the roof timbers would need to be those that do not affect bats.

The final 'inhabitants' to be included in this section may seem rather strange, and there is certainly no known method of detecting them, and that is ghosts. Whether the surveyor, author or indeed the reader believes in such phenomena is not at issue here, but what is certain is that some people *do* believe certain properties to be haunted, and this belief, if it becomes widespread, has been shown to have an effect upon value. Investigations by a colleague of the author have suggested that, while this can have an adverse affect upon domestic property, some commercial properties such as hotels and public houses can actually have their value enhanced by the belief that they are haunted.

10.10 Site and boundaries

This section of the inspection should not be rushed, even though it may be carried out towards the end of the time on site. The general condition of boundary walls and fences as well as details of any significant changes in level and in particular the presence of retaining walls will need to be recorded. Unusual excavation features such as ha-ha trenches cannot always be spotted from ground level, and it will of course be necessary to inspect the site fully, unless the surveyor's instructions exclude this aspect of the property. Assuming that they do not, then the following will need to be inspected:

Boundary walls
Record the construction and general condition. Very often the failure to provide thermal movement joints in masonry walls causes cracking. High brick walls can become a grave danger if they deteriorate to such an extent that they are likely to collapse. Free-standing brick arches are a particular problem, and several injuries a year (some fatal) occur as a result of the collapse of such features. Even relatively new arches can be affected, particularly if there is a heavy gate constantly slamming into the supports of the arch.

Retaining walls
These may be within the property or on the boundary, but in either event they should be inspected very carefully for any signs of deterioration. The existence of adequate drainage through the wall should be checked to ensure that they do not collapse under waterlogged conditions (sometimes there will be land drainage,

Figure 10.1 Structural damage to building caused by failure of retaining wall
(Photograph courtesy of Paul Chaplin)

which is less easily detected). The damage that a collapsed retaining wall can cause is illustrated by Figure 10.1.

Fences
The condition of these should be noted. In general, timber panel fences with concrete posts and gravel boards have a significant life, but those fixed to timber posts have a much shorter life. Older timber fences are likely to require replacement within the foreseeable future. Chain-link and wire-strand fences obviously provide less privacy, and if any fences are not animal proof this matter should be reported to the client. As indicated in Chapter 5 the solicitor will usually advise the client about the responsibility for the maintenance of the boundaries.

Hedges
Without some additional fencing these may not be animal proof. The maintenance liability of hedges should be stressed in the report.

Trees
The problems of trees in close proximity to buildings have been discussed in Chapter 8. If there are any large trees or hedges (or any that have the potential to become large) these should be noted. As indicated previously, one authority recommends that the surveyor carry a pocket identification book of trees.[3]

Pavings

The construction, condition (any unevenness or cracking) and approximate age of all pavings should be recorded. Asphalt drives in particular can cause problems: what can appear to be a recently paved drive at the time of inspection can deteriorate rapidly if it has been laid by itinerant workers for a few (black economy) pounds. The maintenance liability of pea-shingle and gravel drives should be commented upon in the report. Drainage arrangements for hard pavings should be considered; it may not be raining when the survey is carried out. In period terraces the steps leading to the front door can often form part of the weather protection for part of the cellar (sometimes originally used as a coal store). As these age they deteriorate, and this may lead to dampness problems in the basement.

10.11 Outbuildings

Outbuildings will not be inspected to quite the same level of detail as the main building, but it is important that any serious defects are recorded – particularly to the garage. A structure housing what may be a very expensive vehicle is expected by many clients to be in a similar condition to the main building. Yet the garage is something that clients frequently look at only superficially when viewing a property, and it is up to the surveyor to advise them whether, for instance, the flat roof requires recovering or whether the overhead door will not actually open. Other outbuildings are very often poorly maintained, and the necessary advice for placing such structures back into good condition should be provided by the surveyor. The cost of demolition and reinstatement of outbuildings should be included in the fire insurance valuation.

10.12 Non-standard construction

This section is particularly applicable to housing but also has some relevance to commercial buildings. The vast majority of houses in the UK are of traditional masonry construction, but in the inter-war period and immediately after the Second World War a variety of system-built houses were constructed, and timber-framed houses became increasingly common during the second half of the twentieth century. The identification of these 'non-standard' methods of construction is essential when carrying out any type of survey. This is because certain types of non-standard house are not considered to be suitable for mortgage lending by the financial institutions. This obviously affects their market value.

The surveyor will quickly become familiar with the various types of non-standard houses built in his or her area: most of these were originally built by local authorities but may now be privately owned. Generally all brick- and tile-clad timber-framed houses are suitable for mortgage lending except those where the 'cavity' has been filled with insulation after construction. Typical defects with timber-frame houses were largely due to poor site practice and have been identified as:

- *Omission of the vapour barrier.* This should be at least 500 gauge polythene or equivalent, and must be fixed to the warm side of the insulation. Fixing should be delayed until the frame has a moisture content of 20% or less. Any holes for services should be neatly cut, and all tears should be repaired with special tape.
- *Excessive notching and cutting of studs.* Any cutting of the structural members to receive services should have been kept to a minimum and carried out in accordance with the recommendations of the designers of the frame.
- *Base structure.* It is important that the base structure was 'square' to avoid any problems of frame assembly and fixing. This could result in the cavity between frame and cladding becoming too small so that there is an increased risk of rain penetration. If the base was not level, minor inaccuracies could be overcome by packing the sole plate.
- *Wall panels.* If not erected vertically an uneven cavity with the possibility for rain penetration could result. Breather paper should be fixed, with generous laps.
- *Cavity barriers.* Good supervision is essential to ensure that these are not omitted, as their absence is almost impossible to detect.
- *Protection.* Incomplete treatment of the timbers, usually as a result of poor quality control, increases the risk of rot. Inadequate weather protection can result in distortion as the frame dries.[4]

Few of these potential defects can be adequately checked during a superficial inspection, but problems as a result of these defects may be detectable. There have also been a number of high-profile problems as a result of failure to tie the brick cladding adequately to the frame, and evidence of bulging or non-vertical brickwork should be looked for when surveying timber-frame buildings.

The most common system-built houses were the Airey type (easily recognised by its 'shiplap' concrete cladding) and steel-framed houses, but there are well over 30 types that were built throughout the UK. Following an investigation by the BRE of a fire in an Airey house in the early 1980s, some 24 systems were designated by the Housing Defects Act 1984 as being houses for which grants were available to carry out remedial works (often involving complete replacement of the external walls with traditional construction). Steel-framed houses were never grant aided, and no further grants for any system houses remaining are now available.

10.13 Summary

The main matters discussed in this chapter (external joinery, partitions, decorative condition, floors, ceilings, internal joinery, chimney-stacks and external works) are the subject of fewer professional negligence claims than the matters discussed in the two preceding chapters. However, a thorough and professional inspection of these items is still of course required.

Now that our inspection has been completed and copious notes have been taken, we shall consider how we should write our survey report.

Notes

1 *Assessment of Damage in Low-rise Buildings* BRE Digest 251 (Building Research Establishment, Watford, 1990).
2 A. Dunster and I. Holton 'Assessment of ageing high alumina cement concrete' *Structural Survey*, Vol. 18 (2000), No. 1, pp 16–21.
3 M. Hollis *Property Services. Part 2: The Exterior* (The Chartered Surveyors' Education Channel Video, 1995).
4 D. Marshall and D. Worthing *The Construction of Houses* (Estates Gazette, London, 2000).

11 Writing the report

11.1 Importance of the report

So far great care has been taken to ensure that the client's conditions of engagement have been confirmed, that the necessary surveying equipment has been assembled together, and that a detailed inspection has been planned and executed. However, all of this effort will have been completely wasted if the surveyor fails to write an acceptable report. The service the surveyor provides will be judged entirely upon the contents of the report.

Report writing is an extremely important skill for the surveyor to acquire, and it is vital that this skill be developed before the surveyor ever reports to a client about the condition and state of repair of a building. Traditionally it has been developed in surveying practices by reading other surveyors' reports and by the trainee surveyor inspecting a building at the same time as an experienced surveyor, writing a 'shadow' report and comparing this with the actual report prepared by the experienced surveyor. It is only by serving this apprenticeship that the trainee can be sure to develop the essential skills before carrying out the first survey for a client. The trainee is of course likely to have studied report writing as part of his or her built environment degree course, but this does not by itself adequately prepare the surveyor for the real world of surveying buildings.

The practice will also wish their new surveyor to comply with their corporate report writing style, and although in some firms there is scope for individualism in report writing many other firms employ libraries of standard phrases so that their reports comply with this corporate identity. Part of the firm's quality assurance procedures will require that the first few reports prepared by a new surveyor be very carefully checked by a supervising surveyor, who will also have inspected some of the properties. The lack of this adequate supervision of young surveyors has been identified as one of the principal causes of professional indemnity insurance claims against surveying firms. It has been suggested that this careful 'minding' of junior members of any professional practice is an essential facet of true professionalism.[1]

11.2 Writing style

Clients will not tolerate poor grammar and spelling in their reports, which should be written in the third person (avoiding personal pronouns such as 'I' and 'my'). Although most survey reports will contain some technical detail, no prior technical knowledge of the client should be assumed. It is thus necessary to explain technical terms where these cannot be avoided. Therefore instead of simply referring to the 'wall dpc' some phrase such as 'the wall damp-proof course, which is a horizontal layer of impervious material, provided at low level in masonry walls and designed to prevent moisture rising from the ground to the interior' should be used. When referring, for example, to a rafter it should be explained that this is 'an inclined roof timber', and so on.

As indicated above, each surveying firm is likely to have its own style of report, and surveyors will probably be encouraged to adopt standard paragraphs or phrases. Information technology, and in particular word processing, has made such practices much easier and more widespread. There are commercially available libraries of such terminology, and surveyors using these systems are encouraged to merely select the appropriate clauses when writing the report. Indeed the individual drafting of a report to suit a particular property is nowadays quite rare. Even if surveyors do not formally adopt such a method of report writing they will soon find that they are using similar sentences over and over again when drafting reports.

Such practices certainly have their place in a highly competitive marketplace, but it is important to be aware of the possible drawbacks of such systems. First, each property is individual, and no two buildings are identical. There will always be some aspects of a survey report that are specific to that particular property and which will require individual drafting. Second, it is tempting to believe that because a report is compiled largely from tried and tested phrases it is not necessary to proofread the report quite so carefully. This view is extremely dangerous: such reports require just as careful proofreading as an individually drafted report. The author was once shown a survey report that in consecutive paragraphs contained completely different descriptions of a roof covering. It was quite obvious that two rather than a single (appropriate) standard clause had been used, and that the surveyor had failed to notice this fact when proofreading the report.

Technology has now moved on further, and some firms are using voice recognition software to prepare reports. Thus the need for a secretary to type reports has been removed. This software has become increasingly sophisticated, and provided some effort is taken to train the computer adequately, surprisingly good results can be achieved. With this type of report it is even more important that very careful proof-reading is undertaken. No court of law would find in the surveyor's favour if their only defence was that the computer had misunderstood what they had dictated!

11.3   Reporting defects

In Chapter 7 advice on site note taking was offered, and very similar advice is applicable here. For each element of construction it is necessary to report the following:

1. design and construction
2. condition
3. cause of any defects (or recommended further investigation).
4. remedial work required.

In addition it has been recommended[2] that for each particular defect the surveyor should advise on:

1. worst case and ultimate risk
2. extent of work necessary
3. complexity of work
4. expense of work
5. his or her opinion of what is happening.

Advising on the cost of remedial work is of course fraught with difficulty. Say for example that the surveyor was to advise that a roof covering was likely to cost £4000 to replace, and the lowest quotation the client could obtain after purchasing the property was double that amount: then one would expect that a claim would be forthcoming. When advising on the cost of work the surveyor should wherever possible obtain quotations from contractors or, where this is impossible, advise the client to do so before entering into a legal commitment to purchase or rent the property.

Typically when inspecting any building the actual percentage of the structure and fabric that can be viewed is quite small – around 10%. However, the surveyor is expected to use his or her knowledge of construction technology and previous experience to alert the client to possible dangers. Thus if there is no subfloor ventilation at ground floor level and high moisture meter readings are obtained in the adjacent walls the surveyor would be negligent not to advise a more detailed inspection of the floor to check for possible dry rot problems. Thus the surveyor must give advice on areas that cannot be viewed if the evidence suggests that there may be a problem.

When reporting on defects they should be placed in context: that is, the client should be advised if a particular defect is usual or unusual in a particular type or age of property. If every house in a 1930s seaside suburb is likely to be suffering from cavity wall tie problems then the client should be advised of this fact. Following this advice, if the client is prepared to have the necessary remedial work carried out then he or she will purchase the property; if not then he or she will look elsewhere. Such an approach should ensure that clients are not discouraged from purchasing a building just because it has defects. The important thing is that they purchase with a full appreciation of the condition and the work required to remedy the defects. This point is relevant to what the author has previously termed the *surveyor's ethical dilemma*.[3] As indicated in section 3.2 most survey instructions result from recommendation or referral from a third party – usually another professional (normally a solicitor or estate agent), but sometimes a satisfied client. If every client is discouraged from purchasing each property surveyed, then these sources of new instructions will rapidly dry up. Thus, if defects are found, these should be placed in their correct context, and the client should not be warned off purchasing a property just because it has similar defects to every other property in a particular locality.

In the wall tie corrosion example used above, one of the recommendations, following say the discovery of regular horizontal cracking in the external walls, would be to arrange for a specialist to inspect the cavities with an endoscope. Such advice would be quite acceptable (although, as indicated in Chapter 6, some 24% of surveyors in a recent research project indicated that they generally or occasionally use an endoscope). However, as discussed in Chapter 4, care must be taken in recommending further investigation by specialists. The surveyor needs to aim for a balance between cost to client and surveyor's liability, and should not recommend further investigation for work that he or she is capable of doing and/or should have already done.

11.4   Other considerations

Verbal reports should be avoided unless they are complete, and the client should be advised to read the full written report before entering into any legal obligation. In today's busy world it is common practice for people to read only the summary of a report. Therefore the summary must be complete, and it should not introduce any new material not included in the main body of the report.

The author has adopted a method of making a list of the main points of a report as he dictates or types it. The drafting of the summary is therefore a fairly easy matter once the report is complete. An alternative method is to delay drafting the summary section until the main body of the report has been proofread. The disadvantage of this method is that the client may contact the surveyor before the summary is written, which will make it difficult to provide a complete verbal report. It is for this reason that the author always prefers to draft the full report as soon as possible after the inspection.

After many years of carrying out building surveys the author is convinced that his best reports are those that are dictated in the car while sitting outside the property and before returning to the office. Critics of such an approach suggest that this method allows insufficient time for reflection. However, one can always refer to any technical literature or say speak to the local building control officer at the time of proofreading, and when returning to a busy office the surveyor usually has precious little time for reflection. Another advantage of this method is that should any detail have been missed during the inspection it is an easy matter to jump out of the car and record the missing information. It is not so easy to do this when dictating the report at home or in the office 20 miles away.

The summary usually contains a standard limitation clause, which the surveyor's professional indemnity insurer will insist upon. Therefore it is common to read such a final sentence in a report as 'We have not inspected covered, unexposed or inaccessible parts and are unable to say that any such parts are free from defect.' While limitation clauses are legal, their use is severely restricted by the Unfair Contract Terms Act 1977 and the Unfair Terms in Consumer Contracts Regulations 1994, and each allegation of negligence would be considered on its merits. Thus in the floor dry rot example used above it is likely that reliance upon this particular clause would fail. If however asbestos was later discovered in an area to which the surveyor could not possibly have gained access, and there were no other reasons to suspect that asbestos had been used, then this clause might well succeed. Limitation clauses need to be included in the original conditions of engagement to be enforceable. In drafting standard conditions of engagement surveyors need to be aware of the Unfair Contract Terms Act and Regulations. The latter require consumers to be given the opportunity to negotiate contract terms, which suggests that the client's explicit attention should be drawn to any limitation clause at the time of taking instructions.

In any claim for professional negligence that relied upon a limitation clause it would be up to the surveyor to convince the court that the clause was reasonable. The court would apply the principles laid down in *Smith v Eric S Bush* 1989,[4] which are:

- Were the parties of equal bargaining power? If they were, the requirement of reasonableness is more easily discharged than if they were not.
- How difficult is the task being undertaken to which the clause applies? If the task is very difficult or dangerous there may be a high risk of failure, which would be a pointer to the requirement of reasonableness being satisfied.
- What are the practical consequences of the decision on the requirement of reasonableness? This involves the amount of money potentially at stake and the ability of the parties to bear the loss involved, which in turn raises the question of insurance.

11.5 Typical headings

When carrying out an intermediate-level service such as the Homebuyers Report the format of the report is standard and free text is entered under predetermined headings. In drafting a building survey report the headings used are entirely at the discretion of the surveyor.

The RICS Homebuyer Survey and Valuation uses the following headings:

A Introduction
The main conditions of engagement are referred to and the objectives of the report are stated. The only free text to be entered here is the surveyor's overall opinion of the property.

B The property and location
B1 *The property*
Type and age, construction, accommodation are stated here.
B2 *The location*
Brief details of the location are provided, including any adverse matters.
B3 *Circumstances*
Weather conditions, details of any occupiers, of inspection, whether the property was furnished etc.

C The building
C1 *Movement*
See Chapter 8.
C2 *Timber defects*
See Chapter 8.
C3 *Dampness*
See Chapter 8.
C4 *Insulation*
See Chapter 9.
C5 *The exterior*
See Chapter 8.
C6 *The interior*
See Chapter 10.

D The services and site
D1 *The services*
See Chapter 9.
D2 *Drainage*
See Chapter 9.
D3 *The site*
See Chapter 10

E Legal and other matters
E1 *Tenure*
Whether freehold or leasehold, rents, service charges etc. payable.

E2 *Regulations, etc.*
Any statutory matters such as listed status, contravention of Building Regulations etc.

E3 *Guarantees, etc.*
Timber treatment, dpc, etc.

E4 *Other matters*
Any other matters which need to be brought to the attention of the client's legal advisors.

F Summary

F1 *Action*
Urgent repairs, any specialist reports or quotations to be obtained prior to purchase.

F2 *Maintenance considerations*
Any less serious matters that will require expenditure in the future.

F3 *Other considerations*
Any other matter to be reported to the client.

G Valuation

G1 *Open market value*
Value in present condition.

G2 *Insurance cover*
Reinstatement value and gross external floor area.

The report is then signed and dated. The 'Description of the Homebuyer Service' (the conditions of engagement) is attached to the report.

The headings that the author generally uses for a building survey are indicated below. The main information conveyed in each section is as follows:

- **Instructions:** The name of the client, the date of signed acceptance of written conditions of engagement. The date(s) of inspection, the weather conditions, details of occupation, whether property was furnished and/or carpeted.
- **Situation:** Orientation, approximate dimensions to any adjacent road junctions, nature of area, land use in immediate vicinity, street lighting, any restrictions on parking.
- **Description and accommodation:** Type and age of property. Overall plot size and brief description of accommodation and outbuildings. Details of tenure.
- **Site and boundaries:** Description of site, approximate guide of levels of garden, description and condition of boundaries, and liability for upkeep if ascertained.

- **Roofs:** Description in sufficient detail to enable the reader to be able to visualise the roof layout, details of all coverings, estimated age of covering, details of condition, estimated life remaining, any remedial work required.
- **Rainwater goods:** Materials, ages, condition including evidence of any leaks or reverse falls. Details of discharge into drains: separate or combined, soakaways. Any remedial works required.
- **Roof space:** Access points, roof construction, evidence of any rot or insect infestation, slopes felted/boarded, evidence of any leaks, condition of party/gable walls, insulation, any water tanks and condition.
- **Chimney-stacks:** Number, locations, number of flues, materials including flashings, condition in roof spaces, presence of chimney-breasts and if not how supported, flues in use, ventilation of redundant flues, condition of used flues including presence of linings.
- **External walls:** Construction, materials, wall thicknesses, solid or cavity, condition, any evidence of movement, causes, assessment of age of movement, likelihood of continuing movement, dpc, any high moisture meter readings, subfloor ventilation.
- **External joinery:** Materials, design, condition, next redecoration required, any evidence of rot to timber joinery. Include windows, doors, any weatherboarding, roof fascia and barge boards.
- **Internal doors:** Type, materials, condition, any requirements for fire doors, any remedial works required. Condition of ironmongery.
- **Internal walls:** Loadbearing, non-loadbearing, condition, any evidence of movement, decorative condition.
- **Floors:** Solid or suspended timber, concrete, dpm, boarding, extent of any fitted coverings, deflection evident, adequacy of subfloor ventilation, any evidence of rot or insect infestation, remedial works required.
- **Ceilings:** Type, condition of upper surfaces (in roof space and by raising floorboards), age, estimated life, decorative condition, remedial works required.
- **Staircases:** Type, materials, balustrades and handrails, any problems with design or headroom, condition, remedial works required.
- **Fire insurance:** Gross external floor area, reinstatement value.
- **Services:** Types and ages, materials used, estimated lives, extent of any testing carried out or required, remedial works required. Include water, electricity, gas, drainage, heating installation.
- **Sanitary fittings:** Types, materials, ages and condition including expected lives. Include bathroom, WC, utility room and kitchen fittings.
- **Outbuildings:** General comment on overall condition including any major defects.
- **Summary (and valuation):** Complete but concise list of all work required and general comment on overall condition. Open market valuation

in present condition if required. Any standard limitation clause required by insurers.

The report is then signed and dated.

11.6 Summary

Provided that the surveyor's detailed inspection is reflected in a carefully written and adequately proofread report, then the client should receive an excellent service. But the best inspection will be of little worth without a well-drafted report. In order to reinforce the very important concepts discussed in this chapter a case study of an actual building survey report is presented in the final chapter of this book.

Notes

1 D. Maister *True Professionalism: The Courage to Care About Your People, Your Clients, and Your Career*, p 144 (The Free Press, New York, 1997).
2 M. Hollis *Property Services. Part 4: The Report* (The Chartered Surveyors' Education Channel Video, 1995).
3 M. Hoxley 'How do clients select a surveyor?' *Structural Survey*, Vol. 13 (1995), No. 2, pp 6–12.
4 *Smith v Eric S Bush* (1989) 2 All ER 514, HL.

12 Case study: building survey report

12.1 The good, the bad or the ugly?

Just as in life we learn best from our mistakes, so when undertaking surveys the most enduring lessons are those provided by our errors. Hopefully these will not be too expensive for the new surveyor or his or her firm, but in an increasingly litigious society even the smallest error seems to have the habit of developing into an expensive claim. What is certain is that no surveyor is ever likely to progress through his or her career in the modern world without facing the unfortunate circumstances of a claim for professional negligence. Hopefully by adopting a thoroughly professional approach in preparing for the survey, inspecting the building and writing the report, such claims will be few and far between.

The presentation of an excellent example of a building survey report in this final chapter was considered, but instead it was decided that far more would be learnt from the analysis of a rather poor report. However, this report is not a work of fiction but an actual survey report carried out by an experienced surveyor within the last 10 years. In fact the survey is an early example of a seller's report, as it was commissioned by the agents engaged to dispose of the property by auction. The report was given to all parties viewing the property before the auction. Obviously the names of the surveyor and the property and location details have been amended so that complete anonymity is respected. Apart from these changes the report is reproduced exactly as it was produced, warts and all, and there are plenty of these. At least 20 spelling or grammatical errors have been identified. As will be seen from the penultimate paragraph of the report the surveyor has sought to excuse these deficiencies in presentation on the grounds of having to provide the report at short notice.

The commentary is based on an inspection after the survey was carried out. It is recommended that the report be read initially without reading the commentary. This will enable readers to then compare their views with the commentary, when undertaking a second reading.

Overall the surveyor's opinion is valid: that the property is structurally sound and requires extensive modernisation, but provides a new owner with the opportunity to restore it without having to undo the work of others. However, there are a number of problem areas where the surveyor has left him or herself vulnerable to potential claims.

12.2 Ambridge Hall, Ambridge, Borsetshire

Ambridge Hall is a seven-bedroomed, two-storey house constructed in the Georgian style about two hundred years ago and having a separate staff flat at ground floor level. The house is located in a rural position and occupies a plot of approximately 7.5 acres. The report of Joseph Grundy follows (comments are contained in the bullet points at the end of each section):

Building survey of Ambridge Hall
Location and description

The property comprises a detached country house dating from the late 18th Century and approximately 200 years old.

The construction is conventional in solid brick elevations under pitched and tiled roofs with solid and suspended timber floors. The main structure which is approximately square has two storeys; the extension containing part of the self-contained flat is single storey with a single slope lean-to roof.

The house faces east and is constructed on a more or less level site in a semi-rural location between the villages of Ambridge and Darrington. It is located some 4 or 5 miles to the north-east of Borchester.

The survey relates to the house and immediate outbuildings only. No inspection of the gardens or land being sold with the house has been made.

It is understood that the property is listed Grade II as of architectural and historic interest. Close to the house stands a former Coach house now utilised as garages and stores and also further storage buildings constructed of brick under a single slope slate roof. There is also an area of walled garden to the west of the house.

- There is some tautology in the first paragraph, as it is not really necessary to give both of these figures.
- There is nothing to say when the inspection was carried out or what the weather conditions were at the time. In view of comments made later about the watertightness of the rainwater goods the client would be entitled to believe that there was heavy rainfall at the time of the inspection.
- There is no mention of who the client is or how conditions of engagement have been confirmed. (Fellow *Archers* fans may suspend belief a little longer by assuming that the clients are a Mr and Mrs R. Snell.)
- The distance from Borchester is rather imprecise: the surveyor should have checked his or her car mileage from the office.

- The surveyor has advised the client that the property is Grade II listed but nowhere in the report have the full financial implications of this fact been emphasised.

Accommodation

The accommodation is as follows:

On the ground floor:	*Entrance hall; Dining room; Staircase Hall; Cellar; Drawing room, Sitting room; Rear hall; Cloakroom; Staff sitting room; Butler's pantry; Kitchen.*
Separate self contained flat:	*Sitting room; Inner corridor; Utility room; Kitchen.*
On the first floor:	*7 Bedrooms; 2 Bathrooms; Separate W.C.*

- There is probably sufficient detail in this description of the accommodation, but there is no way in which the reader is able to identify which bedroom is which. Some further detail to orientate each bedroom (and to distinguish between the bathrooms) would have been useful.
- No details have been provided anywhere in the report about the plot size, site and boundaries or tenure; the flat was tenanted at the time of the author's inspection

Construction and state of repair

The roofs

The house has a pitched and hipped timber framed roof covered with black glazed pantiles. There is a central flat section with a lantern roof light located above the stairwell and this flat section is covered with bituminous felt. Black glazed pantiles cover the roof slopes including the single slope roof above the single storey rear extension.

It is apparent that the roof coverings have been relaid comparatively recently, probably in the last 2 or 3 years. Roof slopes are even with no signs of any undue deflection or sagging. The black pantiles are mostly the traditional glazed variety, but to some of the inner slopes there are low grade tar-dipped pantiles in evidence.

The pantiles are generally in satisfactory condition and show no signs of any serious decay or failure. Details include tile and cement ridges and hips, and lead valleys and flashings and these are generally sound and sufficient.

The flat section of roof is covered with bituminous felt that was renewed very recently. The felt is in satisfactory condition and shows no signs of any deterioration.

The fall of this roof is to the guttering at the rear. No inspection of the roof light could be made from the exterior. The internal appearance of the timbers is poor and it may be found that some attention is required externally when access is gained to the roof top.

There are four chimney stacks built of brick and mortar. These are more or less square and upright and in fair structural order. Brick and mortar materials have been the subject of repairs in recent years and currently they are in reasonable condition. Flashings are in lead and felt and these are in fair condition, although some moisture penetration to the interior is apparent and this may well require some further attention in the years to come.

The roof framework is approached via access hatches above two of the upper bedrooms. The framework is in original softwood timbers with principal and common rafters, purlins and collars. There has been some recent minor repairs and reinforcements of the framework.

Roof timbers are affected by active woodworm infestation and this will require spray treatment which works should be undertaken by a reputible company with a guarantee provided. Otherwise the timbers are sound and sufficient with no signs of any outbreaks of rot and decay and with moisture content levels within an acceptable range.

The roof is felted beneath the tiles and there was no sign of any water penetration into the interior. However the void area has not been provided with adequate insulation and this work will have to be put in hand.

The single storey extension is provided with a roof framework in softwood timbers that are of a similar age to that of the main roof structure. Timbers are again affected by active woodworm infestation and spray treatment works are required.

- Again there is some repetition in the first paragraph of this section, with 'black glazed pantiles' mentioned twice. This suggests inadequate proofreading.
- There is some inconsistency in reporting, in that the surveyor says that he or she has not been able to inspect the roof light and yet he or she reports on the condition of the bituminous felt-covered roof, at the centre of which is the roof light. Is it possible that the surveyor has in fact not inspected this central area but has accepted someone's assurance that the felt covering has been renewed very recently? There is no comment made about the limited life of bituminous felt coverings to flat roofs.
- In the paragraph about the chimney-stacks nothing is said about the limited life of felt flashings (these are where the stacks abut the flat roof, but should ideally have lead flashings over them).

- There is nothing that most clients take more exception to than dampness problems, and the casual way in which the damp penetration around the chimney stacks is reported is very poor. To suggest that this problem 'may require some further attention in the years to come' considerably underestimates both the problem and the extensive further investigation work required to discover the actual cause of the problem before remedial work may be put in hand.
- Again, the description of the roof construction lacks detail, and technical terms are used without an explanation of what they refer to.
- Reading the final paragraph of this section it is not clear whether the single-storey roof void has any insulation, and the client would be quite entitled to assume that insulation existed. It did not.

Gutters and pipes

Gutters were entirely renewed 2 or 3 years ago in uPVC materials, and these connect to both uPVC and older cast iron downpipes and hopperheads. These in turn connect to trapped gulleys formed of brick and concrete and then to underground soakaways.

Materials are of adequate size and capacity to cope with normal levels of discharge. There was no sign of any leakages to the system at the time of inspection nor is there any evidence of any weeping of joints. Hopperheads require clearing of some debris as do trapped gulleys, which work will have to be carried out on a regular basis.

Cast iron materials show some minor signs of corrosion beneath the decorations. Some attention to these will be necessary in the years to come. There was no obvious above ground signs to suggest any failure of the underground drains or soakaways.

- In this section a clear statement is made that there is no sign of any leaks from the rainwater goods. Since there is no statement about the weather conditions at the time of the inspection we are entitled to assume that it was raining. Presumably the surveyor was not surprised to receive a telephone call from his clients the first time it rained following their taking up occupation!
- It is not clear what 'obvious above ground signs' there would be to suggest failure of the underground drains or soakaways. This comment is superfluous, and leaves the surveyor open to criticism.

The elevations

The main elevations are constructed of solid 13" and 9" red brick with limestone windowcills, rubbed and guaged red brick arches and penny rounded (i.e. the joints are struck with a straight line) mortar pointing.

The walls are upright with no signs of any significant deflection or leaning. There is some evidence of minor settlement that has occurred over the years as indicated by one or two small cracks in the brickwork here and there, for example between the main structure and the rear extension where the brickwork between one and the other has not been keyed in. The movement is of a minor nature, appears to have stabilised and is considered unlikely to continue to any significant extent in normal climatic conditions. The bricks and mortar are genereally in reasonable condition for their age. A number of the bricks are becoming badly spalled however and this is most noticeable at the base of the walls particularly to the east (front) and south elevations. In the years to come it will be necessary to repair the bricks by patching in matching replacement units where the existing are badly weathered.

The bricks are of an age where they have become rather porous and are prone to allowing moisture to penetrate. Some damp penetration was apparent in one or two of the upper rooms. This is a typical problem to be overcome in properties of this type and age. Improved ventilation and heating of the house may assist in this regard and it is advised that the damp penetration is monitored for a while before any decisions are made as to repairs.

The mortar pointing is generally in reasonable condition for its age. Some patch repairs have been carried out here and there in a hard cement based mortar which is proving more damaging than beneficial. It is advised that in the years to come this work is renewed with a soft lime based mortar which will not cause excessive weathering of the brick surfaces. In the years to come some judicious and sympathetic renewal of the mortar pointing may become desirable although such work should only be undertaken by skilled labour.

The cellar retaining walls and floors are formed of brick and concrete which exhibit some signs of moisture penetration and dampness. This is to some extent to be expected and in this instance is not considered particularly serious. Again some patch repairs to the brickwork and concrete may be found necessary in the years to come in order to preserve the brickwork and minimise the possibility of structural failure.

- Again, the way in which the cracking in the brickwork of the external walls is reported is far too casual: 'one or two small cracks in the brickwork here and there'. It is to be hoped that for his or her own sake the surveyor has taken much more detailed notes of the cracking, supported where necessary by sketches, than have been reported to the client.
- The surveyor has failed to diagnose that spalling at the lower levels of the external walls is the result of the lack of a damp-proof course and subsequent frost action.
- Reading between the lines of the third paragraph of this section the surveyor

seems to be in two minds as to the cause of the dampness at first floor level. The initial suggestion is that it is due to penetrating dampness, but the subsequent comment about improved ventilation and heating leads one to suspect that condensation may be thought to be the cause. No one, least of all the client, should have to read between the lines of any part of the report; it should be explicit. The second inspection suggests that the problem was predominantly one of condensation: the dampness was restricted to the north facing bedrooms.

- The comments about a softer lime mortar for re-pointing are good, but again there is some repetition in this section.
- Has any thought been given to dehumidifying mechanical ventilation of the cellar?

Damp proofing

Tests were conducted with an electronic damp meter around the house. Rising dampness was detected in most of the rooms, although in the drawing and sitting rooms dry lining is provided which is preventing any damage to interior finishes.

It is now advised that the property is provided with an injected chemical damp proof course throughout. This work should again be undertaken by a reputible company and a guarantee provided.

- Apart from the surveyor's not being able to spell 'reputable' the advice about installing a dpc is probably correct. However, no mention of the necessary replastering or replacement of dry linings is mentioned. The client would be entitled to feel very aggrieved to discover that this additional work was necessary, and might well seek recompense from the surveyor.

Floors

At ground level there are suspended timber floors in the dining room, drawing room, sitting room and in walk-in pantry.

Elsewhere there are solid concrete floors with a rather cracked stone flag finish in the entrance hall and with a quarry tile finish to the inner hall.

The suspended timber floors are not provided with any subfloor ventilation at all, although the cellar lies partly beneath the sitting room where ventilation is improved.

Moisture content in the floorboards was found to be in the high range and given the absence of subfloor ventilation it is likely that outbreaks of woodworm exists beneath the floors and it is possible that some outbreaks of rot and decay are occurring in joist ends. There appears to be no wholesale failure of the floors to date and if any remedial works are found to be necessary these are likely to be repairs rather than wholesale renewal. In addition it is advised that an adequate number of airbricks are provided in the foot of the walls where there are suspended timber floors.

The flag stone and quarry tile floors are uneven and cracked with age and are affected by some levels of dampness. If required they can continue in use as existing, although any covering of these floors with carpeting is likely to lead to an unacceptable build up of moisture. The concrete floors in the kitchen and in the rear self-contained flat are in such poor condition as will necessitate total renewal.

To the upper storey the suspended timber floors are partly visible and are in softwood with boards running largely from front to back and with joists from side to side. In some of the rooms there is fitted carpet throughout and a thorough inspection was possible only in isolated areas. Joists are exposed in one or two places only.

The floorboards and subfloor joists at first floor level are affected by active woodworm infestation and spray treatment works are now required. There were no outbreaks of rot and decay apparent, although the flooring will be at risk in places where dampness has entered into the structure, for example from porous 18th century brickwork and poor chute work in gutters and pipes. One suspect area of this kind is to the floorboards adjacent to the damp reveals inside the separate WC at first floor level, and also to the joists in the vicinity of the washbasin in bedroom 7 where damp penetration from the exterenal brickwork is particularly in evidence. These areas should be exposed for further inspection when it is possible to do so.

Part leakage or failure of plumbing and sanitary appliances may also be a cause for decay in floor timbers. Again it is impossible to know the extent of such problems in areas of the bathrooms and WC and this will only become evident when it is possible to fully expose the floors.

- The advice about the lack of subfloor ventilation and the need to provide it is appropriate, but the dangers of possible dry rot attack and the need for further investigation should have been made much more explicit. The surveyor does not indicate whether any floorboards were raised; this should certainly have been done as part of a full building survey.
- The comment 'there appears to be no wholesale failure of the floors to date' seems certain to fill the client with confidence! There are very few instances in which the word 'appears' would be appropriate in a survey report. Either something is or it isn't. To use the words 'appears' or 'seems' is invariably to suggest that the surveyor lacks confidence in his or her opinions or advice.
- Again, the surveyor's failure to be explicit about which floors are covered is a serious failing. He or she will not be able to rely upon lack of access to raise floor boards without saying which floors it has not been possible to inspect in detail.

- The term 'poor chute work in gutters and pipes' is rather antiquated, and is at odds with the comments made by the surveyor under the heading of 'Gutters and pipes'.
- Based on the second inspection it is believed that the damp flooring in the separate WC and Bedroom 7 has far more to do with leaking plumbing and sanitary fittings than with dampness penetrating through the walls. The surveyor also seems to have come to this conclusion rather late, judging from the final paragraph of this section. However the reader is left wondering just what is the cause of this problem.

Joinery

Windows throughout the house are of the vertical sliding sash type, double hung in box frames. These have been fairly well maintained over the years although some further repairs are now required. There are some fixed opening lights which require easing and adjusting, for example to the entrance. Also in bedroom 1 there are broken sash cords. In addition one or two of the glazing panes are cracked, for example in the dining room. The timber sill to the main bathroom window is rotted and in need of repair. Given these repairs and regular maintenance the sash windows should continue to function adequately for a fair number of years to come. Other external joinery comprises the lantern light above the stairwell, the panel and glazed front door with classical timber surrounds. In addition there are timber and glazed rear doors. The lantern has been referred to earlier in the report. The doors and timber surrounds to the front door are generally in reasonable condition with no signs of any serious failures.

Internal joinery comprises two staircases, timber panel doors with softwood architraves and skirting boards, a variety of fitted and built-in cupboards and the kitchen and utility fittings. This is mostly original and of reasonable quality. Some of the doors are now slightly mishapen by slight structural settlement and/or deflection of floors which has occurred over many years. This is to some extent a normal problem to be overcome in this type of property.

Joinery is affected by wear and tear, but there were no signs of any outbreaks of rot or decay where I was able to inspect. Please note it was not possible to lift skirtings etc. to view the undersides. Given some minor repairs and reinstatement the existing joinery should continue to function adequately for a fair number of years to come. The joinery is included in the listing of the house and any alteration or removal of it will require listed building consent.

- Some sensible advice is given in this section, but the surveyor has not made explicit the fact that because of the listed status of the building any new owner would not be able to provide replacement uPVC windows.
- For the first time a personal pronoun (I) has crept into the report.

Plasterwork and partitions

Ceilings throughout the house appear to be entirely the original of early lathe and plaster construction. These are cracked and in some places sagging slightly with age. One section in the staff sitting room has failed and has been cleared away ready for repair. Elsewhere the ceilings to the upper landing and in bedroom 1 are badly cracked. That in bedroom 4 as been overlaid with plasterboard leaving little of the ornamental cornice on view.

In terms of the character of the property it is desirable that these ceilings are repaired rather than renewed with plasterboard. They are quite capable of repair. Repairs should be carried out where the ceilings are starting to fail and are sagging and where they are badly cracked. Again such work should be undertaken by skilled labour.

Internal partitions are formed of both brick and timber stud and plaster. These are more or less straight and upright and show no signs of any structural movement or failure. Internal plastered finishes are again very old and mostly original. Some damage to the plasterwork has occurred where dampness has entered into the structure, for example to the upper landing and in some of the bedrooms where penetrating dampness is apparent. Patch repair of the plasterwork will again be necessary.

- No comment apart from the fact that presumably the ceilings are of 'lath' and plaster.

Decorations

Internally the house is in need of total redecoration. Externally the paintwork is in fair condition but in places is starting to become worn and peeling to some of the surfaces and renewal will be necessary in the next year or two. In the meantime some touching in may become necessary to areas where paint is peeling badly in order to protect the timbers beneath.

- It is unusual to combine internal and external decorations in one section like this. The external decorative condition is best dealt with when reporting upon the exterior.

Sanitation and services

Drainage

Foul waste drains from the property by means of 4.5" cast iron soil pipes on the flank and rear elevations. This connects to an underground drain that runs beneath the rear of the property and to a septic tank behind the stable block on the north side. The drains are 6" diameter in glazed clay. They are badly silted and affected by root penetration and undoubtedly subject to leakage. The tank is very old and one of its chambers could not be reached. It is apparent that the tank is in working order. Its brick and concrete construction is showing signs of deterioration and will require renewal in the course of the next few years. It is advised that the work should be put in hand in the context of any major renovation of the property.

- The surveyor has said that the drains are undoubtedly leaking, but has said absolutely nothing about replacing them. The client will assume that it is OK to do nothing about these leaks.
- Although the surveyor has offered the more sensible advice that the septic tank is likely to require renewal in the next few years, he or she has said that it is in working order. It is impossible to give this advice based upon a simple inspection at one point in time. If the clients were to discover, after one week of using a washing machine twice a day and a dishwasher once a day, that the tank is unable to cope then it is going to want replacement very much sooner than advised by the surveyor. Who do you think is likely to be paying for the replacement?

Water supply

Water is supplied to the premises from a main located beneath a cover in the tin shed outside the backdoor of the house. Water is pumped to the property at present. Mains water is available from the nearby road and could be connected to the property without too much inconvenience. If it is intended to continue with the existing supply adequacy of the well and pumping machinery should be established as should the quality of the water.

- Owing to what is probably a typing error this entire paragraph is extremely confusing. What the surveyor should have said is that there is a well (not a main) in the tin shed. A first reading suggests that mains water is connected, and again because of failure to proofread this report adequately it is possible that the surveyor will be paying for this mains supply to be connected.
- The property is surrounded by arable farmland, and therefore checking the quality of the water for nitrates and other chemicals will be a high priority.

Hot and cold water services

Hot and cold water services are provided around the house in a mixture of lead, cast iron and copper pipework. Some of this is run externally and will be prone to frost damage. One of the cold water systems is galvanised metal and is unhygenic. The hot water system is awkardly located in the kitchen. It is advised that in the context of modernisation and improvement of the property that hot and cold water service installations will have to be entirely renewed.

- Careful proofreading would have led the surveyor to change 'system' to 'cistern' on the two occasions it appears in this paragraph (as well as

hopefully to correct other spelling mistakes – the typist has obviously not heard of a spell checker).
- The need to replace the plumbing and tanks is clear, but the surveyor has not mentioned the health hazards of lead pipework.

Sanitary fittings

The present sanitary installations are old and it is assumed that all kitchens and bathrooms will be refitted in the course of refurbishment and updating.

- Good advice, but we are never told anywhere in this report just what fittings exist at the moment.

Electrical installation

The electricity meters and switchgear are located in the ground floor flat. Electrical wiring in PVC is installed around the house and this is some 15–20 years old. The work was undertaken to a simple specification with a limited supply of light and socket fittings and much surface run ducting. We would advise that this be disregarded in your consideration of the purchase so that total rewiring of the building should be undertaken as part of overall refurbishment.

- Good advice.

Heating

There are fireplaces located in the main reception rooms and in some of the upper bedrooms where they have been covered. Where the flues could be inspected they were found to be in original brickwork. If it is intended that fireplaces should be put into regular use it will probably be necessary to introduce flue linings to the existing brick chimney flues. The remaining chimney breasts are structurally sound.

There is no central heating to the property although one or two old night storage heaters are apparent here and there. Otherwise there is a dependance on portable electric heaters.

- The advice about lining flues to be used is correct, but ventilation of redundant flues should also have been recommended.
- The use of the term 'remaining chimney-breasts' suggests that some may have been removed. If so, details of support should have been provided.

The outbuildings

The stable block is constructed of 9" brick with a pitched and hipped timber framed roof covered with pantiles. The building is generally dilapidated with a missing window to one flank wall, failing plaster ceiling and walls to the attic room and woodworm in roof and floor timbers. Creeper growth is penetrating the roof in places which should of course be discouraged. Walls are affected by some moisture penetration and by rising dampness. External masonry would benefit from brick and mortar repairs.

The brick and slate range of outbuildings is in a poor state of repair with leaking and failing roofs that are overrun with creeper, old and dilapidated doors and joinery and spalled and porous brickwork. The range of timber and tin buildings is also dilapidated and is currently unsightly. The garden wall is overrun with creeper at one end where little could be seen. Elsewhere the tile coping is failing and in need of repair.

These are a number of trees growing close to the foundations of the house, notably the holly and oak at the north-east corner. These should be trimmed back or removed to prevent the possibility of root action from affecting foundations. There is also Virginia and other creeper on the house which should not be allowed to overrun and clog gutters etc.

- The descriptions of the outbuildings and the comments about their overall condition are at about the correct level of detail.
- It is believed that there is a clay subsoil in the area in which the property is located. The advice about trimming or removal of vegetation may therefore be inappropriate, as such work could lead to heave of the foundations.

Conclusions

It will be apparent from the above report that while the property has some advantage in being largely unaltered from its original form, the extent of updating that is now required is considerable. Nevertheless the structure and fabric constitutes sufficient base for the necessary repairs and improvements although the costs involved are likely to be high. To properly repair the house and to update the service installations and to provide central heating and to under-take basic repairs to the outbuilding, we think it would be necessary to allow a budget cost of between £40,000-£45,000 to which VAT presently at 17.5% must be added. This approximate estimate would not include any updating of kitchen or bathroom fittings. Obviously any expenditue on refitting will depend upon the extent and quality of work required and there may well be some overlap with repair costs.

It is hoped that this report will provide sufficient information for your purposes. The report has been prepared at short notice and we apologise if any minor errors have crept in as a result.

This report should be read in conjunction with the Conditions of Engagement already notified to you.

JOSEPH GRUNDY
For RODWAY AND WATSON
SURVEYORS
BORCHESTER

Date

- There is no summary of works required provided nor any standard limitation clause.
- The estimated costs of the remedial work are on the low side.
- It would have been safer to advise that estimates be obtained prior to exchange of contracts.

12.3 Concluding comments

In addition to the above commentary, the surveyor's use of English is rather poor. Some phrases are repeated several times: for example, 'here and there' and 'more or less' seem to be great favourites. Another criticism is that there is a lack of both technical detail and precision throughout the report. Although verbosity is not to be encouraged, this report is far too short, bearing in mind the size of the house. Had the headings recommended in this book been adopted then it is likely that more detail would have been incorporated. The failure to adequately identify exactly which floors were covered and exactly where the external wall cracking was, for example, may cause the surveyor problems in the event of a complaint or claim.

The author has no idea whether the eventual purchaser of the property relied upon this survey report, but had he or she done so then it will be seen from the discussion in this chapter that the probability of a claim resulting will have been high. There is no guarantee that, if readers follow every piece of advice offered in this chapter and throughout this book, they will not be sued. However, by following the advice given and by acting in a thoroughly professional manner the chances of such an unfortunate event will be greatly reduced.

Happy (but careful) surveying!

Further reading

Introductory

M. Hollis *Property Services. Part 1: The Aims of a Survey* (The Chartered Surveyors' Education Channel Video, 1995).

M. Hollis *Property Services. Part 2: The Exterior* (The Chartered Surveyors' Education Channel Video, 1995).

M. Hollis *Property Services. Part 3: The Interior* (The Chartered Surveyors' Education Channel Video, 1995).

M. Hollis *Property Services. Part 4: The Report* (The Chartered Surveyors' Education Channel Video, 1995).

M. Hollis *Surveying Buildings* (RICS Books, Coventry, 2000).

D. Marshall and D. Worthing *The Construction of Houses* (Estates Gazette, London, 2000).

I. Melville, I. Gordon and P. Murrells *Structural Surveys of Dwelling Houses* (Estates Gazette, London, 1992).

P. Parnham and C. Rispin *Residential Property Appraisal* (Spon Press, London, 2001).

RICS *A Guidance Note for Surveyors: Building Surveys of Residential Property* (The Royal Institution of Chartered Surveyors, London, 1996).

RICS *A Guidance Note for Surveyors: Building Surveys and Inspections of Commercial and Industrial Property* (The Royal Institution of Chartered Surveyors, London, 1998).

I. Seeley *Building Surveys, Reports and Dilapidations* (Macmillan, Basingstoke, 1985).

Advanced

A. Bravery, R. Berry, J, Carey and D. Cooper *Recognising Wood Rot and Insect Damage in Buildings* (Building Research Establishment, Watford, 1997).

BRE *Assessment of Damage in Low-rise Buildings*, BRE Digest 251 (Building Research Establishment, Watford, 1990).

CIC *Definitions of Inspections and Surveys of Buildings* (Construction Industry Council, London, 1997).

CIRIA *Structural Renovation of Traditional Buildings*, CIRIA Report 111 (Construction Industry Research and Information Association, London, 1986; reprinted 1994 with update amendments).

A. Coday and M. Hoxley 'The portable test equipment being used for commercial building surveys' *Structural Survey*, Vol. 19 (2001), No. 4, pp 173–184

D.W. Dixon and C. Scivyer 'Radon and remedial measures' *Structural Survey*, Vol. 17 (1999), No. 3, pp 154–159.

A. Dunster and I. Holton 'Assessment of ageing high alumina cement concrete' *Structural Survey*, Vol. 18 (2000), No. 1, pp 16–21.

M. Hoxley 'How do clients select a surveyor?' *Structural Survey*, Vol. 13 (1995), No. 2, pp 6–12.

IStructE *Subsidence of Low Rise Buildings*, (The Institution of Structural Engineers, London, 1994).

D. Maister *True Professionalism: The Courage to Care About Your People, Your Clients, and Your Career* (The Free Press, New York, 1997).

RICS *Surveying Safely: A Personal Commitment* (The Royal Institution of Chartered Surveyors, London, 1991).

P. Robson *Structural Repair of Traditional Buildings* (Donhead Press, Donhead St Mary, 1999).

SAVA *Benchmark Standards for the Homebuyer Survey and Valuation* (Surveyors and Valuers Accreditation, Woking, 2000).

D. Wilkin and R. Baggott 'Technical factors influencing decisions to select underpinning on shrinkable clay' *Structural Survey*, Vol. 12 (1994), No, 2, pp 10–14.

C. Wood 'Death-watch beetle and its treatment' *Structural Survey*, Vol. 17 (1999), No. 3, pp 131–137.

Index